THE EMBATTLED LADIES

OF LITTLE ROCK

1958 – 1963: THE STRUGGLE TO SAVE PUBLIC EDUCATION AT CENTRAL HIGH

Vivion Lenon Brewer

LOST
COAST
PRESS

Fort Bragg
California

D1160892

THE EMBATTLED LADIES OF LITTLE ROCK

1958 – 1963:

THE STRUGGLE TO SAVE PUBLIC EDUCATION

AT CENTRAL HIGH

CONTENTS

PREFACE

by Patricia Murphey Rostker

Well into the middle of the twentieth century, "Jim Crow" ruled the South. Blacks were segregated from whites and forced to submit to demeaning and discriminatory practices. Public schools, transportation, movie theaters, restaurants, and even water drinking fountains were strictly segregated. Then, on May 17, 1954, The United States Supreme Court, led by Chief Justice Earl Warren, unanimously ruled that racial segregation in public schools was unconstitutional. The popular United States President, Dwight D. "Ike" Eisenhower, was all but silent upon this significant ruling. The political climate in the nation's capital was one of apathy and aversion to the grievous problems of segregation, while the political sentiment in Arkansas was markedly segregationist.

Things began to change on December 1, 1955, in Montgomery, Alabama. Rosa Parks, riding a public bus, refused to relinquish her seat to a white person. She was arrested, and a protest movement under a twenty-five year old Baptist minister named Martin Luther King, Jr. was launched. As one of the leaders of the boycott sparked by Rosa Parks, Martin Luther King was threatened and his house bombed. He was jailed and beaten, but one year later the Supreme Court ruled that bus segregation was unconstitutional.

Some Southern states attempted to evade the school integration law by establishing schools for black students that were "separate but equal." Nobel prize winner William Faulkner was pilloried in the Mississippi press for calling for higher standards of education for all students, regardless of race. Waving a hatchet, Governor Wallace proclaimed that Alabama would defy federal law, but the battle lines were most clearly drawn by Governor Orval Faubus in Arkansas. In 1957, he ordered the Arkansas National Guard to bar admission to nine black students seeking entry to the previously all-white Central High School in Little Rock.

Forced by federal order to withdraw the National Guard, Governor Faubus looked on as the 1957 school year proceeded with black students at Central High. In September of 1958, however, rather than permit further integration, Governor Faubus shut down all four of Little Rock's high schools.

Little Rock was paralyzed: both black and white students were locked out of their high school classes, and parents were desperate to get their children back in school. Into this hotbed of social and political unrest, riots and boycotts, where previously only Rosa Parks, Martin Luther King and a small handful of others had marched, a small band of white ladies appeared, determined to open the schools in Little Rock, no matter the color of the students. Patronizingly chastised for meddling in the affairs of men, these ladies persisted, and recriminations grew as the ladies' efforts started meeting with success among the anxious citizens of Arkansas. When threats could not deter the ladies, secret and cowardly "enemies" planted bombs, mailed hate letters, and fired their guns at WEC members' houses. However, the movement for equality could be neither ignored nor stopped.

The ladies of the Women's Emergency Committee to Open Our Schools, the WEC, paid dearly for their courage and conviction in the defense of public education for all students. The first Chair of the WEC, Vivion Lenon Brewer, was of independent means and so could not be forced from her job, but her husband, a federal civil servant stationed in Little Rock, lost his position for reasons never clear but patently linked to Governor Faubus's segregationist stand. Other members of the WEC lost their friends and social standing, and families were literally torn apart in the hostile and frightening atmosphere that pervaded Little Rock, and the eyes of the nation turned upon this Southern city that had become a symbol of racism.

This is the story of the WEC. Posterity is fortunate that Vivion Lenon Brewer, one of the three founders and the first Chair of the WEC, kept not only a journal of the struggle to open, through integration, Little Rock's high schools but also the correspondence, newsletters, announcements, proposals, surveys, campaign strategies, and even hastily scribbled meeting notes in an attempt to document the WEC's battle. These documents later provided important organizational tools for use by ensuing groups and ad hoc committees working to bring the South into compliance with federal law. A portion of this extensive material is presented in the Appendix of this book. *The Embattled Ladies of Little Rock* offers the reader a historical record of the fight to retain public education through peaceful integration, as well as source material for those persons and organizations who remain engaged in the ongoing struggle for education, equality, and diversity. For the sake of historical accuracy, the terms used for African-Americans, though "politically incorrect" today, have been retained.

On a personal note, it has always been a badge of honor that Vivion Brewer was my aunt. She set a shining example for me of compassion, warmth, and human dignity. She showed me how to love and care for people even while fighting for social change. My husband and our children were blessed to know her, and many people have told us how Vivion touched their lives for the better. I want to thank my oldest daughter Margaret for undertaking the responsibility of publishing this book. Thus, on behalf of my entire family and the friends of my aunt, I publish her book as a reminder that we must never take for granted public education, equality, and the courage of personal conviction.

P. M. R.
August, 1998

FOREWORD

This manuscript is gratefully dedicated to all the women who gave their time, energy and talents to the Women's Emergency Committee of Little Rock, Arkansas in the years from 1958 to 1963.

My inexpert fingers apologize to my Smith-Corona Electra 120, and I offer special thanks and apologies to Dorothy Yarnell Barton and to Karen Mercer Fite who tried to teach me something about the written word.

I wish also to express my sincere appreciation to the *Arkansas Gazette* to the many quotations which have ramified my memory.

I feel vastly relieved to have all of this record on paper, after thinking about it with good intentions for twelve years while being absorbed in more active pursuits of the elusive spirit of brotherhood. It saddens me that these troubled times convince me that it is not advisable to make this manuscript available to the public now. I relinquish it to libraries* with the hope that it may prove of some value to students in the years to come.

V. L. B.
Thanksgiving Day
November 23, 1972
On Bearskin Lake
Scott, Arkansas

---

* The original manuscript and all appendixes are housed in the Smith College Library.

INTRODUCTION

In the fall of 1957, nine Negro students registered
at the formerly all-white Central High School in
Little Rock, Arkansas. Governor Orval E. Faubus,
needing a gimmick to assure his reelection to a third
term in 1958, seized upon this "threat" of integration and, assuring the public that he knew there
would be violence, sent in the National Guard to
surround the high school. On September 4, the nine
students attempted to enter Central High but were
repulsed by the Guard. An emotional crowd, there
"because the governor asked us to be," followed the
young blacks with shouts and curses. It was a press
photographer's picture of this scene which made
Little Rock an international symbol of hatred and
racism. Federal Judge Ronald N. Davies subsequently ruled that Governor Faubus had not used
the Guard to preserve law and order and enjoined
him and the National Guard from interfering with
integration. On September 20 the governor removed
the National Guard, and on September 23 the Negro

students quietly entered Central High School by a side door. Waiting and watching, a crowd of some thousand whites, urged on by a "friend of the governor," fought and wept, and battled impotent police. The next day, September 24, President Dwight D. Eisenhower sent the 101st Airborne Division into Little Rock and the National Guard was mobilized under federal orders. There followed a year of litigation, rumor, frustration, fear, and harassment.

In July of 1958, Governor Faubus was assured a third term in the primary. In August he called a special session of the legislature and sponsored a bill which provided a means for the governor to close the public schools. The bill was quickly adopted. When the United States Supreme Court, on September 12, 1958, decreed that integration had to proceed immediately at Central High School, Governor Faubus signed a proclamation closing Little Rock's four high schools. This was on September 15, the day the high schools were to have opened belatedly. The elementary and junior high schools had opened two weeks earlier.

On September 16, the Women's Emergency Committee to Open Our Schools (WEC) was organized and I became its chairman. The story of this committee, the first group in the South which rose to defend public education, albeit integrated, should be of record. People at home and all over the world have asked me what motivated the organization of the WEC, how I became involved, and why I was willing to act as chairman and bear the brunt of malicious and often vicious harassment. This, therefore, becomes partially a personal history, so let me begin by sketching my background and reflecting upon the evolution of my philosophy.

My parents, Clara May Mercer and Warren Ernest Lenon, married in Guthrie Center, Iowa, on December 25, 1889. My mother was a handsome woman of unlimited drive and energy. Before her marriage, she taught all grades in a one-room school in rural Iowa, walking miles to reach it. During her married life she was an ardent club-woman and an efficient organizer with a great variety of interests. My father, son of a miller and one of eleven children, set out at twenty to find his fortune. By chance he settled in the small but booming capital of Arkansas. There he found a job in an abstract office, one of whose owners was a Negro. Although he had only a high school education, he was always a student. In time his advice was sought by business and professional men and even by attorneys. He had a pervasive interest in the development of Little Rock, and was elected mayor in 1902. His was a career of service to his city. A prominent businessman said to me in 1959, "If your father had been alive, none of this would have happened in Little Rock."

I was born on October 6, 1900, just two blocks from the present location of Central High School. I grew up in a happy, devoted family, the middle one of three children. When I graduated from Little Rock High School at sixteen my parents sent me to Smith College in Northampton, Massachusetts. Even more unusual than choosing a college so far away was my parents' permitting me to go to Europe after graduation to meet a college friend and travel for fourteen months.

My major had been sociology and I had envisioned myself a social worker in the slums of New York. My first summer at home after college however, I decided to learn typing and shorthand and so took a job as a stenographer in the People's Savings Bank, which my father had organized soon after my birth. There were so many things to learn that I also enrolled in the night classes of the Arkansas Law School. I widened my financial experiences with a fling at being co-owner of The Little Gift Shop.

I know that I grew up in a carefully segregated society with traditional Southern prejudices. These may not have been as ingrained in me as in others whose families had lived longer in the Deep South, but they were there and I lost them only gradually. Until we were six and entered our respective schools, Tessie Lee Ola Phoebe Ann Goella Sims, the daughter of our family cook, and I were bosom friends. Yet I was not at all puzzled when our paths sharply diverged. This was just the way it was. When I went North to college there was a brilliant Negro girl in my class, but we never knew each other. I recall contemplating her scholarship with envy at the same time wondering how I'd feel if we chanced to walk out of the chapel side by side. I was surprised, though somehow not shocked, to find an attractive Negro family in the congregation of the Baptist Church in Northampton but I never came to know them. In the South I had seen Negroes only as servants, although often beloved servants; or as polite but often obsequious customers at the bank; or as "happy" occupants of dilapidated plantation cabins. I do not recall wondering at this. I do remember proclaiming, "In my next life I want to be a plantation Negro." The memory of my own blindness helps me to understand the blind spots of my neighbors in this plantation country.

One specific experience which caused me to question some of my earlier ideas occurred soon after I graduated from college and returned to Little Rock. As a child and young adult I had an unmarred attendance record at the First Baptist Church, of which my mother was a dedicated member. Yet I first read the Great Book in one of my college courses. Somehow word of this trickled back to the most orthodox of the fundamentalist Baptists in my home town, and soon after I started working in the bank, I was invited to a quiz by a delegation from my church. They had heard that I no longer believed in the Bible; they had heard that I had doubts about the literal interpretation of the story of Adam and Eve. I was told that I would be a very bad influence on the young and I was asked not to attend the church in the future. It may be of interest that in years to come this church acquired a far more illustrious member in Governor Orval E. Faubus.

For a long time after this I went to first one church, then another, but gradually I found more awareness of the presence of God in the miraculous pattern of nature. This was never a problem to me until I became chairman of the WEC. Then I had to work out a formula. In the South, any questionnaire is apt to include the all-important "church affiliation." In fact, it is quite disreputable in our Bible Belt to die without one's church prominently noted in one's obituary. At the beginning of workshops, each participant may well be asked to announce not only her name and occupation but her church as well. For a while I responded with: "I was brought up a Baptist"; however, I always felt that this was quite dishonest even though it was the literal truth. Eventually I decided on something which was not true at all but which in its implications more nearly satisfied my sense of integrity: "I'm interdenominational." It has always seemed a curious comment on our practices that this ridiculous statement never raised an eyebrow or elicited a query.

In 1930 I decided I wanted to marry Joe Robinson Brewer more than I wanted to continue my career as vice-president, director and trust officer of a bank. We met at the Democratic Convention in Houston, Texas, in 1928, the year his uncle, Joe T. Robinson, for whom he worked, was nominated vice-presidential candidate on the ticket with Al Smith. We were married in October 1930, and moved to Washington, D.C. where Joe developed his government career, as secretary to the Majority Leader in the United States Senate. After Senator Robinson's death, Joe worked in the personnel offices in the Departments of Justice and Interior. When war intervened, he served in the Office of the Chief of Staff of the Air Force, and subsequently in France and in Berlin with the United States Control Group. He was to be gone such an indefinite time that I decided to rent our home in Foxhall Village and to live with my father, then a widower.

My father and I both loved the summer house he had built sixteen miles east of Little Rock. Despite the lack of modern facilities and equipment, we decided to stay there, and it was during those months that I realized that Joe and I had better not wait to retire there. We must make the move while we were young enough to tackle the job of developing the place as a year 'round home. That story would make a book, but there is one pertinent aspect of these years that I must mention. When Joe returned to take the position of Personnel Officer at the Veterans Administration Hospital in North Little Rock in 1946, and we were beginning to learn how to live in the country, we both took a long, hard look at the feudal plantation life surrounding us. In Washington, D.C., a "bright" woman had been not only our cook and maid but my companion through a protracted illness. She had taught me much about the fears, the trials, and the prejudices, as well as the mores of her race. Yet our exposure to the problems of the Negroes in the Nation's capital and our concern for them had not prepared us for the problems of the Negro sharecroppers and tenants. The extent of the poverty appalled us and we were even more dismayed by the illiteracy. I began to teach the few Negroes living nearest us, both adults and children, to read and write, and came to know the effects of racial discrimination.

Suddenly we were confronted by that disgraceful September day in 1957 at Central High School in

Little Rock. The stories friends told me of that violence which need never have been except for the egocentric ambition of one supremely shrewd man, served to heighten my anxiety over the "place" of the Negro in the American way of life. All that winter and the next summer, stories of the indignities heaped on those courageous young Negroes in Central High School, who wanted nothing but a better education, drove me to a state of illness. And I worried about the wider implications. I worried about the possible destruction of a once beautiful, peaceful and progressive city. With the threat of closed schools, I worried about all the young people, our future citizens, who would be denied an education. I worried about the emotional effect on them which could produce such long-lasting residuals. I worried about their being taught total disregard of law and order. I worried about the effect of the events in Little Rock on foreign relations. In short, I was sick with it all.

Joe and I had planned to take our first trip together to Europe that summer of 1958, but I couldn't face feeling my deep personal shame if I were asked about Little Rock. It would ruin our travel. Instead we decided to drive west to some of our National Parks. That was a mistake. Every place we stopped grim or sarcastic faces, glancing at our Little Rock license plate, demanded an explanation: "What goes on there?" The climax came in Yellowstone when a student employee at a filling station near Old Faithful refused to service our car until Joe cornered him and made it very clear how we felt. Our vacation was a flop.

Back home the end of August, nothing but the beauty of the lake at our door cheered us. Then one day in September as I returned home from town a neighbor asked, "Did you hear about yesterday?" I hadn't heard. It seemed that David Moore, a Negro man who lived on a near-by plantation and occasionally helped us with difficult chores, had been fishing with his wife in a boat near the bank. Maybe he had had a heart attack or maybe he just leaned too far to one side, but whatever it was, he suddenly fell into the water and disappeared. His agonized wife screamed for help. There were a few boats on the lake, but no one wanted to get wet enough to try to rescue David.

That evening, Ernie Baldassare, a young Navy frogman on recruitment duty in Little Rock, heard the tale and hurried there to bring David's body up from the shallow water. The coroner came, but could not be persuaded to do anything but take the body to the morgue. "He's just a nigger," was what I was told he said.

I decided that the least I could do was to take some food and a little money to his family. I had to ask my way to their house across the bayou and back in the fields along plantation roads I had never traveled. What I saw as I approached the shanty is indelibly printed in my memory. One pregnant young woman wearing only a faded, bedraggled skirt, dirty unkempt hair framing her face, was hanging a tattered piece of wet clothing on a wire fence. Another girl, similarly unclothed, nursed a small, nude baby. Three naked little children sat in the dust. The odor made it obvious that the outhouse was any place that was out.

Every face turned to me in stark terror; I managed a broad smile which affected only my mouth. "I'm so sorry about David," I said as I stumbled out of the car. "I just heard about him. I'm so sorry. Is Mrs. Moore here? I brought something for her." Slowly the tableau came to life and the widow appeared in the doorway, still wary. I pushed my packages and a bill into her hand and fled. I was filled with horror and despair, not for them as much as for myself. I found it devastating to realize that I had lived within two miles of this for twelve years and had remained oblivious to it.

This was my mood the morning Mrs. Terry phoned and asked without preamble, "Are you ready to do something about Little Rock, Vivion?"

"I certainly am," I told her.

One

Three Women

It all began one evening in April of 1958 when the Ashmores didn't come for dinner. Joe and I had invited Barbara and Harry Ashmore and three mutual friends to share an informal supper at our home on Bearskin Lake in the Scott community sixteen miles east of Little Rock, Arkansas. That morning Barbara phoned to say that Bitsy, then about ten years old, had an upset stomach which wasn't too serious but which, with all the tensions, demanded parental attention. Our mutual friends, the two Louises and Jimmy came anyway, and as the evening progressed, it was inevitable that we discuss the alarming situation at Central High School, the harassment borne by the Negro students there and the editorials which Harry Ashmore had written for the *Arkansas Gazette*. We applauded the merit of the Pulitzer Prize recently awarded to him and the paper for their courageous position.

Louise Vinson told us that Mrs. David D. Terry, one of Little Rock's most prominent citizens and a lifelong friend of the Heiskells who owned the *Arkansas Gazette*, had felt that a small dinner should be given — perhaps at the Country Club — to recognize the honor bestowed on Harry and on Little Rock's morning paper. Trying to crystallize this idea, Mrs. Terry had asked a friend to seek Louise's opinion. "Well, I just laughed," Louise admitted, "and assured her that nobody would come." She and Jimmy were close to Harry and Barbara and knew that the night the Pulitzer Prize was announced, the Ashmores had had a lonely evening until *they* appeared a little belatedly with champagne and good wishes.

Moved by acute concern for all that had been happening and *not* happening in Little Rock since the infamous Central High crisis in September of 1957, and by sincere admiration for the *Gazette* policy, I hazarded a purely intuitional estimate, "But I am sure three-hundred people would come!" There was an incredulous reaction to this, but I felt an emotional urge to support my sheer guess.

The other Louise egged me on, and Joe backed me with a practical suggestion. With years of experience arranging dinners for a thousand participants in an annual Psychiatric Institute at the Veterans' Administration Hospital, he volunteered, "I'll make all the arrangements for the dinner at the hotel." Louise Vinson agreed, a little skeptically, to get our messages back to Mrs. Terry.

This was all the impetus we needed. Mrs. Terry later admitted that she had had no notion of a large affair but, encouraged by our optimism, she had wondered, "why not?" She called to her home a sizable committee of men and women, and enthusiasm spread. As he promised, Joe served as chairman for all of the arrangements at the Marion Hotel. I spent many long days with a small group cataloguing and mailing invitations, filing reservations, delivering tickets. We kept a complete list of those invited and their response or silence, and this file in time became a political asset. Dozens of friends of the *Gazette* became involved and the success of the dinner is history. On the night of June 3, the overflow from the main ballroom spread into the balcony, the ante-room, and finally to the lobby. As Ralph McGill talked, the room grew very warm and my mind wandered to reflections on the diverse assembly. I wondered how many echoed the sentiments expressed in the *Gazette* editorials. It was reassuring when later comments signified that for well over 800 Little Rock residents, at least for a few hours, the magnolia curtain was raised by this testimony to a courageous newspaper.

Joe and I drove home, momentarily elated. It did not matter at all that Harry Ashmore was not cognizant of our share in the planning, nor that it was highly probable that the owners of the *Arkansas Gazette* were quite unaware of our existence; this was the modest beginning of our stand for human dignity.

I had known Adolphine Terry from my first year after college when I joined the American Association of University Women, the Little Rock branch of which she had helped organize. Since her graduation from Vassar in 1902, her good works for her city, her state and mankind had been legion. She says, "I came home from college determined not to be a Southern lady," but this she is in the best sense of the term: a vital woman with a gracious personality, and a keen sense of humor, compassion, courage, and wisdom (see Appendix 1). As Harry Ashmore said to five hundred of Mrs. Terry's friends honoring her at a banquet in the 1960s, she had long ago recognized that racial segregation is as "irrational as it is immoral, and rejected the practice in her personal life and set forth resolutely to do what she could to temper its manifestations even while the dubious doctrine remained imbedded in the law of the land." For over forty years she was interested in the problems of segregation and integration. When local citizens would have nothing to do with it, she helped organize the Phyllis Wheatley Branch of the YWCA for Negroes. With pride she watched developments as Little Rock advanced beyond most Southern cities in race relations. The Public Library was desegregated, as were the Children's Hospital, the Ministerial Alliance, the University Medical School, the bus stations, the Girl Scouts, the League of Women Voters, the transportation system (although by custom the Negroes never ventured to sit in the front of the buses), and some industries. All the state colleges had a desegregation policy, although there were pitifully few Negroes enrolled in them.

Recalling the events of 1957-58, she told me: "When the governor saw a chance to further his political career and caused all the trouble at Central High School, I wanted to die. I felt my life was completely washed out, and I sank back in my misery, trying to forget the world. But I didn't die, and when the women of Winfield Church invited me to talk about the World Council of Churches meeting in Evanston, which my life-long friend Blanche Martin and I had attended, I got up and hunted up the news clippings and notes which I had brought home from that meeting, put away without re-reading and forgotten. Wholly without enthusiasm, I started sorting and reading, and I came upon the notes on a sermon which Bishop Debelius of Germany had delivered. His text was 'Lose not your confidence for in keeping of it there is great reward,' and he told of the way America had helped Germany after the war and how a day of prayer was planned with the expectation that maybe 6,000 souls might attend — and 60,000 came. Suddenly I forgot my will to die. If the Bishop of Germany, a Protestant Bishop serving people still behind the iron curtain, can bring such a message, why should I despair?"

The first thing Mrs. Terry did was to go talk with Mrs. Faubus. Mrs. Terry had given a party for her and for her husband soon after he was elected governor the first time, and so they met as friends. Mrs. Faubus told of how their only child, a son Farrell, had been harassed or ignored by his fellow students at Central High School. Apparently the parents of most of the pupils had supported ex-Governor

Cherry, whose family had been very popular socially in Little Rock, and the resentment over his defeat carried over into malevolence toward the son of the new governor. Farrell had been very unhappy and finally they had sent him back to Huntsville, their home town, to the high school there. Mrs. Faubus thought that her husband was only too glad to have the chance to bring disgrace on Central High School, and that neither she nor anyone could sway him from this mood.

"But I went home and wrote a letter to Mr. Faubus," Mrs. Terry continued. "I told him that I had supported him two times, that I considered him bright and that these troubles were no solution to the problem of desegregating the schools. I pointed out the fact that few people had the opportunity to be great, but he had been given the chance to be really great by thinking of a positive solution. I quoted Deuteronomy 30:19 — 'I have set before you life and death, blessing and cursing; therefore choose life.' Perhaps he never received the letter; it was never answered."

So she sat down to think of what might be done in the prolonged silence of the city fathers, and she remembered a regional meeting of the AAUW in Hot Springs some years before, when a woman from Atlanta had spoken of an organization of Southern women opposed to lynching and had urged members of various women's groups to join in this crusade. "I felt that these women were really responsible for the fact that lynching was no longer a popular diversion and I decided women who worked together could accomplish great things." She wrote to Atlanta for all the obtainable information about that organization.

Just at this juncture, Mrs. Terry received a letter from a young woman, Velma Powell (see Appendix 2), who had lived in her home for a year while attending a Little Rock business college. Then secretary of the Arkansas Council on Human Relations, Velma had made lists of things she thought could be done to improve race relations and the over-all situation in the schools. Time after time, she pondered these lists and talked with her Negro friends about them, but no one knew how to begin. Finally in September of 1958, Velma decided to write to Mrs. Terry. Her letter read something like this: "In the past, whenever problems have had to be faced in Little Rock, you have taken a lead in solving them. Why are you silent now? Where are you?"

"It all fitted in somehow," Mrs. Terry explained, "so I called Velma. She felt all that was needed was for someone to speak out. People would follow. She was insistent that we try. But who would be the leader? Velma suggested that Vivion Brewer might do it and I thought of the success of the Pulitzer Prize dinner and Vivion's part in it, and my courage grew. So I phoned her and asked her to come see me."

Two

The Rigged Election

On the Friday afternoon of September 12, 1958, Adolphine Terry, age 76, Vivion Brewer, 57, and Velma Powell, 36, faced each other in the parlor of the Terry Mansion, sitting beneath the portrait of Mrs. Terry's father in his Confederate uniform. Believing without reservation that all people are far more alike than they are different and that hatred is insanity, we pooled our anxieties. We agreed that it was useless to continue our stunned silence of the past year during which we had waited for the men of affairs to do something. We discussed the methods of the anti-lynching organization and decided to emulate them. This might be a long range educational program, but anything was worth trying. Race relations were steadily worsening. If ever there was a time to act, this was it; if ever there was a place to begin, it was Little Rock. "We'll do it," Adolphine exclaimed, "and I want you,

Vivion, to be the chairwoman, and you, Velma, to be the secretary."

Each of us took a pencil and a sheet of paper and listed the names of every Little Rock woman who might be induced to come to a meeting designed to organize a study group, an unpublicized gathering to consider possibilities for influencing the climate of opinion toward racial tolerance. Over the weekend, we three spent much of our time on the telephone, but I was handicapped by the eight-party line I shared with unsympathetic neighbors. So after I'd spent hours in a pay booth in town, I retreated to the quiet of our home to jot down some concrete plans and to outline potential committees.

We had hoped for, at most, twenty-five women at our first meeting, so the following Tuesday, September 16, we were elated to greet fifty-eight women in the parlors of the Terry home. We asked each one to sign her name as she arrived. These signatures provided an interesting record: it was not very long before the meeting started to fragment; three of the women called later to ask that their names be stricken from the list.

Mrs. Terry welcomed her guests with a brief reference to the critical year 1957-58 at Central High School. She emphasized the manner in which Governor Faubus, a few hours after the Supreme Court had affirmed the order for the integration of Central High, had closed all four of the high schools under the dictatorial powers given to him by the special session of the legislature that summer, saying, "The next move is not mine; it's up to the federal government." She presented a curtailed history of the anti-lynching movement and proposed that we develop such a group to combat the forces destroying the peaceful progress of race relations and threatening the welfare of our city. She then gave a flattering description of my capabilities and nominated me for the chairmanship of the group. Quite confused by this railroading and the general purpose, the voters assented and I stood up, notebook in hand, making no attempt to be coy about my selection.

As I outlined plans for making studies of race relations and contacting Negro women who shared our convictions, a few women quietly slipped out of the house. When I suggested that, since we were nearing United Nations week, we might ask Marian Anderson to come to Little Rock for a concert, several women vanished. Suddenly a woman in the rear of the second parlor jumped up from her folding chair and cried out, "This is all very fine, but what are we going to do now, *now*? My two boys must have an education and they have already lost two weeks of school. I think we have to do something now to open our schools." There was a clatter of affirmation and I looked from one to another of the intense faces and knew there was nothing to do but throw away all my notes and start over.

The governor had set October 7 as the date for an election in Little Rock in which "the people will decide whether or not they want integrated schools." It was obvious that this was our greatest danger and so must be our first project. Quickly Velma was elected secretary, and Ada May Smith, whom I had met as we worked over the lists for the *Gazette* dinner, was selected treasurer. With the help of some volunteers I appointed a small election committee and, catching the eye of a woman on the front row, I asked if she would be its chairman. Dottie Morris, wife of Dr. Woodbridge Morris, was taken by surprise but with the grace and resolute purpose which characterized the women throughout the life of our organization, she agreed. Promptly she offered her home for a conference the next morning.

"We'll have to have a name now," I mused aloud, realizing that our notions of working very quietly must be abandoned, and I asked Miss Hildegard Smith to choose her committee and come up with a proposal for a name as soon as possible. "We must meet again very soon. Shall we say day after tomorrow, Thursday, here, at the same time? We must plan strategy and organize necessary committees. Our time is so short." It was shorter than I knew, for once our opposition to his policy was known, Faubus advanced the date of the election to September 27, a Saturday when many Little Rockians would be in Fayetteville for a Razorback football game. That left us just eleven days and increased problems!

When everyone had gone, Adolphine, Velma and I sat together. Out the window had gone our ideas of working to eliminate racial prejudice, but perhaps this oblique approach would be even more effective. It would take great caution, however, and there was one thing which must be rectified immediately. *We could afford no hint of being in favor of integration if we were to win any election* in the hysterical atmosphere which our governor knew so well how to foment. This meant that Velma Powell, presently employed as the secretary of the Arkansas Council on Human Relations, a bi-racial organization, a subsidiary of the Southern Regional Council, could not be our secretary. A telephone call and Mrs. Woodbridge Morris agreed to serve in this capacity. Acting without license, as it became necessary to do so often, I automatically considered her elected, "explaining" at the next meeting that Velma's job was too time-consuming to permit this added responsibility.

That night, Barbara Ashmore told Harry about this confused and confusing meeting, admitting she had little idea what would come of it. Who did? Probably this led two reporters to call both Mrs. Terry and myself, but as we had agreed to do, we both said, "No comment." At that moment, neither of us knew what should be said. "The meeting certainly fell to pieces," I had told her ruefully and she had had to agree. The next day, however, following the morning's work of the young women who gathered at Dottie Morris' home, we prepared a statement. This explained our position which was expressed in the cumbersome but descriptive name which Hildegard Smith's committee supplied: Women's Emergency Committee to Open Our Schools, sometimes referred to as the WEC to OSS but in time dubbed affectionately the WEC.

A mimeographed sheet which we distributed widely read in part:

The Committee has been assured by attorneys that there is no possible legal way for our schools to be operated on a private basis without immediately subjecting themselves to further lawsuits which would force them to close again.

Schools operated on a private basis would be deprived of all federal aid, school lunch programs, North Central accreditation, present inter-scholastic athletic competition and eligibility for college scholarships.

To the newspapers I said:

We are deeply concerned that the young people are the ones to bear the hardships of this tragic situation and we are going to do everything in our power to open the four high schools and get the students back in their classes. Since the ballot is to be worded as it is:

<u>For</u> racial integration of all schools within the School District

<u>Against</u> racial integration of all schools within the School District

And we are urging every voter to mark his or her ballot <u>For racial integration</u>, we feel we must classify our position in this regard. We stand neither for integration nor against integration. We are not now concerned with this. Our sole aim — I repeat — our sole aim is to get our four high schools open and our students back in their classes.

Immediately we were news, and my feeling of inadequacy, which persisted as the young mothers discussed detailed school problems, mushroomed. I knew that every word I said must be carefully weighed on the scales of the White Citizens Council, and of the Mothers' League which was then circulating petitions to recall all of the members of the School Board excepting Dr. Dale Alford who was as vocally segregationist as they. I told the local reporters, "I am just a housewife and I have no children, but I grew up in Little Rock and attended the Little Rock public schools. I am convinced that the education of our children is of primary importance to the future of our state. I am neither for nor against integration and we are not concerned with that."

The Associated Press gave me a little testing. A Mr. Ford phoned me: "I have a direct quote from you that you stand for total integration."

"I have not said that," I demurred.

"Then do you favor gradual integration?"

"We are *not* concerned with this," I insisted, hoping the *we* tempered my guilt for the personal lie.

"Well, what is this you say about there being no more free lunches?"

"This is absolutely true," I said, holding my breath for fear he would want a detailed explanation, for this was one of the myriad school data with which I was only vaguely familiar.

I was probably the very worst possible choice for the leader of the WEC. Certainly from a political standpoint I was, although many a time I tried to convince myself that my adversaries would have found something to attack in any woman. I was very conscious of the fact that since our only child had not lived to school age, my knowledge of the facets of modern public education was rudimentary and I did not live in Little Rock. Our home was three-tenths of a mile outside the boundaries of Pulaski County in which Little Rock is situated, although it was included in the Pulaski County Special School District. I had lived away from the state for fifteen years and in the years since our return to Arkansas, my activities had been largely centered in developing our home place; I knew all too few people in Little Rock which had grown so rapidly since 1930.

"I feel so desperately inadequate," I moaned to Mrs. Terry. "No one is adequate to this situation except Faubus," she consoled me cheerfully.

To Mr. James Forman of *The Chicago Defender* I said, "We are *now* concerned neither with perpetuating segregation in our schools nor with hastening integration. Our aim is to get our four high schools open, and we see no other solution than to vote for racial integration." He asked no worrisome questions, perhaps because of the *now*, or perhaps because we — a black and a white — talked together in Mrs. Terry's parlor.

Locally, Bill Lewis seemed to be assigned to me by the *Arkansas Gazette*, although occasionally I talked to Roy Reed. Bill could not have been more pleasant, tactful or cooperative although he was understandably non-commital. On the *Arkansas Democrat*, Little Rock's evening paper, I talked always with Bobbie Forster. I had been warned that she was a threat, possibly an enemy and a very smart one. I found her smart, yes, but always responsive to my requests, friendly and accurate in her reports of my statements.

I spoke with many reporters at Mrs. Terry's. I met reporters in our office. I talked over the telephone with others. I felt pulled in all directions. I was glad to tell representatives from *Newsweek* and *Time*, the *New York Times*, *Chicago* papers, *Des Moines* papers, and everyone I could, that there were people in Little Rock who cared, but I was worried by these demands on the time I needed for study, planning, and supervision. I became overly cautious in my statements. I felt I was not good copy, but more importantly, I believed a prudent course our only hope. Besides, my ingrained aversion to publicity, inherited from my father, made me shy of seeking press releases. However, Jane Scholl of *Life* magazine was insistent that the officers of the WEC pose for photographs and we took valuable hours to assemble for this — Adolphine Terry, Dottie Morris, Ada May Smith and I. The time was wasted. Miss Scholl later told us that we were pre-empted by the American Cup races, but by then I began to realize that four gray heads did not have *Life's* choice of hair coloring. One foreign reporter told one of our women that he was tempted to take a picture of a very pretty young girl on the Capitol grounds and try to run it nationally as the leader of the WEC. I can understand that, remembering the doleful likeness of me which the *Gazette* carried that Sunday ("I didn't want anybody to recognize you," Harry Ashmore apologized), and the picture of our four officers conferring intently. No wonder the White Citizens Council referred to us as "nice old ladies."

"Don't be misled," their large ad read, "into vot-

Members of the WEC Steering Committee, September 1958 (L-R: Barbara Shults, Charlotte Ross, Margaret Stephens, Gwen Booe, Mary Evelyn Lester, Billie Wilson).

Photo courtesy Arkansas Democrat-Gazette

ing for race mixed schools on September 27 by the nice old ladies and the ivory tower preachers."

With the help of Mary Evelyn Lester and Barbara Shults, we hastily found a group of young women who were willing to be publicized as our "steering committee." With cheerful smiles, six of them posed in front of the Terry mansion, (Mrs. L. Prentice Booe, Mrs. Edward Lester, Mrs. S.W. Ross, Mrs. Robert Shults, Mrs. Charles Stephens and Mrs. Gordon N. Wilson) and the *Gazette* featured this picture over the announcement of this new develop-

17

ment in our organization. These young mothers worked, too; they worked tirelessly.

Both local and national radio and TV made demands on our time. This new experience made me quite nervous, for tension affected my control of my vocal chords, injured long ago by three thyroidectomies. I was almost neurotic in my fear of this sort of publicity, but I knew I must try. "Attorneys have assured us," I reiterated, "that because of the necessity of having the use of public funds, the Little Rock schools can not be operated on a segregated basis. We have to choose between integrated schools or *no schools at all.*" I wanted to say, "No matter what Faubus tells you," but I early determined to avoid mentioning his name. I saw only one of these TV appearances, a local newscast and I must say I scarcely recognized myself.

We tried never to overlook any possible help. The announcement of the directors of the Faubus-supported Raney (private) High School included a picture of Mrs. Gordon P. Oates, a club and society figure. Adolphine suggested that I write to her and I did so, hoping publicity attendant on her resignation from this board would influence votes. "As chairman of the WEC," I wrote, "with a group of dedicated women behind me, I am writing to you concerning your position as a member of the Little Rock Private School Corporation. If you are sincerely interested in the public schools of this state, we feel you must realize by now that you could best serve this cause by resigning from the Corporation. I know that you will agree with me that it is imperative that our public schools be reopened, and we hope you realize the only way this can be done is by our winning the election on Saturday. Your influence in the community is so great that your actions influence many votes. We hope you will help us get our schools open."

I mailed the letter special delivery to reach her at her home at the dinner hour. There was no answer. There was occasion to recall this small episode when Mrs. Oates ran for the state legislature in 1960.

Our work was accompanied by a variety of problems and interruptions: rumors flew and needed to be traced; ads of the White Citizens Council stirred prejudice into hatred; Faubus made inflammatory remarks daily (when he returned from the Governors Conference, for example, he charged that the school petition for instructions about leasing buildings was prepared by Thurgood Marshall and handed to Daisy Bates who gave it to Virgil Blossom, and he had this "on good authority.")

Throughout all this the phone rang day and night, and the voices at the other end were too often insolent and insulting, even if they said no more than "Whatcha doin', nigger-lover?" But in spite of all this our work sped along.

Our second full WEC meeting was enthusiastic, and my optimism grew, as over 150 eager women volunteered for committees and specific work. Although I understood with disappointment one efficient young woman's pulling me aside with an agitated, "I can not possibly be on a committee, Vivion, for you know how it would hurt my husband's business in eastern Arkansas," I was thrilled that so many were not only willing but eager to serve. At tables set up on the porch of the Terry home, women signed for many jobs, and in a box in the hall, they dropped slips offering valuable suggestions.

That night, the governor went on TV to explain his plan for a private school. He assured the people that no one need worry about having no high schools; his private school plan was within the law and "even the Supreme Court has not ruled to the contrary." Nor need they worry about accreditation. After all, thousands of private schools were accredited, and the state Board of Education was the accreditor. On September 21 at the Southern Governors' Conference at Lexington, Kentucky, Faubus said, "The Arkansas State Board of Education, not the North Central Association of Colleges and Secondary Schools, is the primary accrediting agency for Arkansas high schools."

Asked to comment on this, Little Rock's School Superintendent Virgil Blossom said, "He spoke correctly. The department accredits schools in Arkansas; the North Central Association accredits schools in Arkansas and eighteen other states."

"Does NCA carry more prestige?"

Blossom: "I know of no accrediting agency that has more prestige."

Q: "Does state accreditation carry less prestige?"

Blossom: "I wouldn't want to say that. I would say that any school that has both NCA and state accreditation could have no higher."

From Urbana, Illinois, the next day came a less equivocal statement from Dr. L.B. Fisher, member of the Association's accrediting commission for secondary schools: "Loss of NCA approval would be a serious blow to Little Rock youngsters seeking a college education."

Even in the face of this Faubus proceeded with his theme song: No integrated school improved education or race relations. He quoted at length the later discredited congressional report on the District of Columbia schools. One of the least inflammatory of the items was the statement that because of integration the IQs in the D.C. schools were two grades lower than the national norm. He stressed all the horrors of sex and illegitimacy. I devoutly wished that people, instead of drinking in his words, would temper them with his own bland remark: "Just because I said it doesn't make it so." Although I had indicated that the WEC might have a statement for the press following this speech, I decided that no answer from us would help. Instead, we were able to secure copies of *Miracle of Social Adjustment: Desegregation in the Washington D.C. Schools* by Carl F. Hansen, the assistant superintendent in charge of senior high schools in the District of Columbia. This documented the refutation of the governor's and the Capital Citizens Council's statements (see Appendix 3), and we distributed the booklet widely, our steering committee members delivering it personally to many a business and professional desk. On our request the *Gazette* published excerpts from it in a news article on our activities.

One of the women who had helped draft our first formal statement had offered us a small room in her business space for an office, but when Dottie Morris and I met her there Friday morning, September 19, we found her very agitated. Her husband had been adamant that she evince no connection with us for fear of reprisals on both of them. This was my second sobering lesson in the necessity of protecting the women who were to work with the WEC. My own willingness to assume a public role was based partly on my naive confidence that my husband's job was protected by his civil service status, but more urgently on the simple choice between trying to overcome the insanity which now reigned in our city or being hospitalized myself.

Dottie Morris and I hastily left the address I had already given to the papers and began to shop for office space. We were fortunate in finding a vacant room on the ground floor of the Capitol Hotel, an early landmark with a beautiful iron Colonial facade. I shall always be grateful to Miss Cassanelli who did not for an instant question our motives, but readily agreed to let us rent this room for an indefinite, hopefully brief time. I promptly phoned the papers that we had already outgrown the space we had rented farther out on Markham Street and had moved to 119 West Markham.

There were several disadvantages in this address. Parking facilities were limited, the rectangular room had no partitions for privacy and the large plate glass windows on either side of the entrance door, opening directly on the sidewalk, made us constantly visible to every passerby and a temptation to hecklers. But we swiftly assembled a desk and a number of chairs, had two telephones installed, one with an unlisted number, and began a frantic week.

We started a scrapbook. We set up some very elementary files. We arranged a schedule for staffing the office daily, except Sunday, from nine to five. Husbands vetoed night and Sunday work at the office as inviting danger when too few people were on the streets and in nearby buildings. We studied the political map of the city, familiarizing ourselves with locations of precincts. We asked for permission to have poll watchers but were told by the Pulaski County Election Commission that this was impossible since there was no candidate to approve them. Mr. Laubach, an election commissioner, did obtain three books of poll tax listings for us and we tore them apart to distribute the pages to women who would call the citizens, urging a vote for total integration *only as* a vote for public education. "Speak always with dignity," I urged. "Be calm and polite. Don't let yourself be drawn into emotional arguments."

We arranged cocktail parties to try to educate everyone we could reach as to the true meaning of the ballot. We printed flyers on vividly colored cheap paper to distribute from door to door. Until one group of teenagers passing out leaflets was harassed by some rowdy boys, we sent high school students down our streets and into public offices and department stores with Save our Public Education propaganda. We set up a group of young people willing to serve as baby sitters while voters went to the polls. We arranged cars for transportation to the polls.

With grave misgivings about our knowledge of public relations, we decided to seek the aid of a professional firm. I called three advertising agencies only to be told, "We are too busy to take another account right now," We doubted the excuse. Then Mary Terry suggested a young man who was with the public relations firm of Ted Lamb & Associates. To my relief, Jim Brandon rose happily, even eagerly, to the challenge and he and I began to spend hours on ads and leaflets, statements for our steering committee members, newspaper ad costs, television and radio possibilities. That I rewrote much of the copy did not seem to antagonize him. In the end, when this phase was all over, I was tremendously flattered and no little amused that Jim wrote me a lovely letter assuring me that I could not have done a better job had I been a man. An accolade indeed!

On the night of September 18, following the first announcement of the formation of the WEC, one of the many phone calls at our home was from the young attorney husband of my niece's childhood chum. Ed Lester was enthusiastically sympathetic. He was one of the sixty-three Little Rock lawyers who were to publish in a couple of days, a full page statement pleading for our public school system. This was, up to then, the loudest voice opposing the governor's plan to operate the schools under a private corporation set up earlier that week. Most of our calls had been vulgarly antagonistic and though

I glowed under his approbation, I cut Ed off. "Now let me tell you what we are planning," he had begun, but I urged, "Ed, let me call you tomorrow. This is an eight-party line and I can tell that it is wide open." How many times I was to repeat that warning.

I did call him, of course, early the next morning and in him and one of his partners, Bob Shults, I found steady support and constantly available advice in the long months to come. To my dying day I will be grateful to them.

Following the governor's talk on TV the week of the election, we appealed to the three local TV stations for equal time to discuss the affirmative side of the September 27 election. John Fugate, of Channel 7, KATV, agreed to give us a half hour on Thursday evening from 6:30 to 7:00 to present our convictions concerning this controversial issue, but Channel 4, KARK, and Channel 11, KTHV, were entirely negative. When the *Gazette* quoted officials of these two stations as saying they had received no request for time from our committee, I was indignant and phoned in a statement not only to the *Gazette* but to the *Democrat*, and when the United Press asked for it, I repeated it to them: "I'm sure there has been some misunderstanding. Both stations were contacted twice by representatives of the WEC and both refused us equal time. John Fugate of KATV offered our committee time in the interest of fair play and his station should be commended for living up to its responsibility to the community to present both sides of this important question. Representatives of our committee will be seen on Channel 7 at 6:30 Thursday night." (Perhaps this is why I was asked to tape a statement for Channel 11, KTHV, the six o'clock newscast for Thursday evening. Of course I did this.)

With a young broker, Walter Trulock, Ed and Bob came to my desk to discuss details of this proposed television program. Two well-known attorneys had agreed to speak. Bill Hadley, for years a news commentator on radio and TV and now the owner of a successful public relations business, would moderate a panel. It was suggested we should have a minister and a teacher or a PTA official. Could we produce them? All too few ministers had spoken out at the time of the riot at Central High in 1957, or since, and some of those who had were transferred out of the state. I knew none of the brave ones personally and so I sought advice. It was not easy to select one to ask nor to find one who would agree to speak on this panel, and after many phone calls, I was grateful to have the Rev. Dale Cowling of the Second Baptist Church readily assent. The PTA Council, wary of the integration problem, had refused to take any stand on the election or even on the closing of the high schools, but Margaret Stephens, a member of our steering committee, who was president of the Central High PTA and whose son had already gone to live with relatives in Dardanelle, Arkansas in order to stay in school, agreed to appear. She was ideal for this role.

Next we sought someone to represent the teachers and since the attorney for the Classroom Teachers Association inexplicably had advised them to remain quiet, this was a problem; but there was a fortunate solution. Marguerite Henry, wife of Dr. Charles R. Henry, mother of three young children, member of the Governor's Committee on Education (GACE), obtained permission from her husband to make a public statement. This made for an effective half hour. Watching it, I felt it had real impact.

Jack Coates, one of my high school classmates, talked on the real issue: What do we vote on in the Saturday election? "The school system will open under court order," he prophesied quite correctly, but "When?" I wondered. Maurice Mitchell, an attorney from the firm of Spitzberg, Mitchell and Hays, assured Little Rock that there could be no private segregated schools financed by state funds and housed in public school buildings. Dale Cowling asked a question which he answered clearly and logically: "Are free public schools worth fighting for?"

Margaret Stephens spoke for the students: "Who stands to lose the most if we close our free public schools?"

And Marguerite Henry clarified another facet of the danger we faced: "If we vote to abolish free public schools, what happens to our teachers?"

Pleased with the success of this program, we decided to pay for one more half hour TV show on Channel 7 for the night before the election, and were sincerely sorry that our speakers had other commitments. Ed Lester, Bob Shults and Walter Trulock worked very hard under the pressure of little time to prepare another effective program. We agreed to ask

27

a minister, a professional man, a representative of labor and a business man to talk on why we wanted and needed public schools. The Right Reverend Robert R. Brown, Bishop of the Episcopal Church, had recently published a book, *Bigger than Little Rock.* Although he had stressed too much, in my estimation, the efficacy of the ministers in the Little Rock situation, I agreed that he would be a wise choice for this panel. He met the four of us at my desk on Friday morning to discuss the program for that night. He agreed that he would appear for us but to our dismay he nullified our format. He was adamant that the other members of the panel must be ministers. Not one of us understood his reasoning and we tried desperately but in vain to persuade him to accept our script.

Deeply disappointed and apprehensive, I picked up my phone to seek three ministers to complete what had become Bishop Brown's panel. Many calls elicited assents from only Bishop Paul Martin of the Methodist Church and Dr. T.B. Hay of the Pulaski Heights Presbyterian Church. Exhausting my list of potentials, with knowledge that the entire script must be re-written within hours, I finally turned once more to the Rev. Dale Cowling. "Of course I'll do it," he said, "but it makes me very sad that you have found so few."

Although Bill Hadley again did a masterly job as M.C., the program attested to its hasty preparation, was poorly timed, blurred in expression, and was a great disappointment. It was an added misfortune that it followed an appearance of the governor during which he attacked the WEC as integrationists and promised that he had a fool-proof way to guarantee the continuation of the existing school system on a segregated basis.

A few days later, two of our members, also members of Bishop Brown's church, called on the Bishop in an effort to understand his position. They felt his explanation satisfied them. Bishop Brown was confident that he had a favorable channel of communication to Orval Faubus and that if this were not disturbed, he could have great influence on the governor. He felt that his appearance publicly as a Bishop with other than ministers would weaken his position. Although I was to confer with him several times in the ensuing months, I was never able to find any basis for his assumption.

On the Tuesday before the Saturday election, a report meeting brought out a house full of earnest women. A membership committee had been busy and, in our notice of this meeting, we had urged every woman to bring at least one friend, assuring them that there would be no pictures taken, no names published without consent. All we asked was the donation of $1.00 to evidence concern, and a willingness to "sign in, please," for we had suspected and had become aware of spies.

Then how could we pay for all we did? We had a clever finance committee, and incredibly, money poured in, often accompanied by such notes as the following:

Dear Mrs. Brewer:

Please find enclosed $5.00 which I hope will be of help in the fight to keep our public schools open. Without public schools and *good* teachers, our future is lost.

I cannot sign my name because my father is in business and I am afraid that Faubus and his friends would try to hurt him.

Best wishes,

A friend

But a few were brave enough to say, "You may use my name should it be of any value." I recall two men particularly, one who at the very outset sent five dollars (and later more) with a signed note from Bryant, Arkansas, and one, a doctor in Little Rock, who cheered us with a generous $50.00. "I am in sympathy with the goal of your organization to open our schools. I pray your group will continue to function beyond the present emergency," he wrote. There were a few large donations. One evening when I was alone at my desk, a plain envelope containing $500 in bills was placed in my hand by a woman who said quietly, "You are not to know where this came from. You do not even know that I have been here." I was quite sure that I did know the source, and the secrecy saddened me, but I comforted myself with the reaffirmation that we were speaking out for many people who dared not speak out for themselves.

This unforgettable week brought me in contact with hundreds of people in my native city whom I had never before known. Indeed the majority of the women who rallied to our call were new friends. Then there were all the other kinds of contact and communication. We received stacks of letters and innumerable phone calls, mostly anonymous. Everyone whose name was identified with us or our motives was plagued by this sort of torment; this was especially true of Mrs. Terry because we met at her home, and of Ada May Smith whose name was signed to our ads that week. She was chosen for this role because we usually urged women to join us by sending their name and $1.00 to our treasurer. Foolishly we added Miss Smith's address and phone number. Very soon it became obvious that, since my name must be known as spokeswoman for the WEC, it should also be used on the ads, but we did specify a post office box for the mailing address.

One of the typical letters I received was: "I'm absolutely dumbfounded at what you and Mrs. Terry are doing. I know her, and I know she isn't a Jew or a Negro, but I do not know you and by your picture in today's paper you could be either or both. Surely you are not an all-white gentile."

Most anti letters were postmarked Little Rock or North Little Rock but some came from afar, such as one from Washington, D.C. that read: "What a stupid ass you are. Are you white or a Negro lover?" One from Kingsville, Texas read: "As mother of five daughters, I do not feel like sitting back and letting a group of spineless women ruin this country just

31

for the sake of a few ornery niggers." My most delightful missive was a card which came in a plain envelope with a typed address, many months after the WEC was birthed:

CERTIFICATE

For valuable services as a traitor to the white
race in race-mixing Little Rock schools, you
are hereby appointed an
HONORARY NIGGER
With all privileges and rights appertaining
to this elevation of your status.
signed
T. Marshall Head Nigger

Often I did not read the letters unless they began with "Vivion," for then I knew they came from persons who did know me well enough to be familiar with the odd spelling of my given name, which is a surname. Not one of these anti letters was ever signed, although the content sometimes convinced me of the identity of the writer. About one of them I was positive enough to discuss it with my devoted friend, Ada Givens, my sister's former maid who came occasionally to help keep our house in order now that I could find no time for it. Years later, an invitation to a party at the home of this supposed letter-writer surprised me to the point of telling Ada about it and asking half-jokingly, "What would you do? Would you go?"

Ada considered this gravely for a moment and advised seriously, "Yes, go, but don't eat anything."

Often Joe took the home phone calls for me and

for the first few weeks he quite enjoyed them, sty-mieing the agitators by quoting poetry, speaking a foreign phrase, asking inane questions, singing a bit of a song. But that grows old and the organizers of this torment seemed to be tireless. It was especially annoying to have the phone ring throughout the night and to answer it sleepily only to hear a receiver click. This was one advantage of the party line, however, for obviously this also awakened our neighbors and somebody finally put a stop to this form of harassment.

We never raised our receiver but we heard a strange whirring click which indicated that the line was open and a recorder set. One night, when I had had to discuss an important plan over our phone, Joe was on the extension and we both heard, after our deliberate silence, "Did you get that, Mrs. _____ (a name familiar to us)? Were you listening then?" We appealed to the telephone company about this but were told they could do nothing unless we'd make a direct accusation. This I did not want to do, for many reasons.

Both letters and phone calls frequently warned us of my imminent death: "Your wife will be hit by a car today and killed."

"Say a last farewell to your wife this morning."

"Do not expect your wife home tonight. She'll be dead."

"You and all others who think as you do should be tied by the feet to a car and dragged the length of Ninth Street as did happen once before." (This was the lynching of a Negro in 1927.)

33

"Arkansas has no air for you to breathe. Go to Washington."

I cannot recall ever feeling any premonition of danger, and if Joe was worried, he did not let me know it. Even when we found bullets on our porch, and shells in our yard, I discounted the danger. As much later as election night in 1962, when we heard shots on either side of our home and found the shells nearby, I knew someone still hoped to frighten us from living here and was convinced we could expect no concern on the part of our county police authorities. I cannot know, of course, how it happened that I drove those miles into town early in the morning, and back again at dusk without even a scare. It seems to me probable that my age and my being a "Southern lady" protected me. I was lucky to escape the crackpots, and my opponents realized that my martyrdom would do more for my cause that my years of devotion to it.

An elderly Negro man, our occasional gardener, was the one who worried about me the most, I suspect, and for an odd reason. He was too devoted to me to broach the subject to me directly, but he explained his anxiety to a mutual friend. "Miss Vivion oughtn't to be doin' what she's doin'," he begged. "You tell her she's goin' agin the Bible and that's a sin, and no use anyway. You know it talks about there's gonna be a beast that'll destroy the world, and sure as shootin', that beast must be Mista Faubus. She oughtn't to mess with him."

Even youngsters attempted to dissuade me. On Thursday afternoon before the election, quite late, after all the other women had gone, I sat at my desk talking with my brother. A slight young boy, below average height for his age which he said was 16, delivered a telegram to me addressed to the chairman of the Women's Emergency Committee. As I read it, he waited, watching me carefully.

As students of Central High, we have already witnessed the evils of forced integration, we feel we have the authority to speak. We do not want any part of integration, gradual or compromise. Some questions we would like for you to answer are: How many of your group have children who will be affected? How many are attending integrated church services? Are you ready to face consequences that follow integration? We use as examples, Hot Springs "integrated working conditions," and Washington, D.C., New York, and other places where integrated schools are a disgrace to our nation. There is no compromise. Segregation is successful; integration is a dismal failure. Common sense teaches us that we should continue the successful practice of segregation. We hope you realize that your group or anyone else that takes the stand for integration will be just as responsible for the blood that might be shed and all other circumstances that follows

integration as Daisy Bates or any of her workers. On behalf of what we feel is the majority of senior high students.

Mike Coulter Carolson

Thomas Billy Hubbs

I would not quote the names except that I felt they must be phony. As I finished reading and looked up, the boy leaned forward over the desk and said, "I was in that fight this morning."

"Would you like to tell me about it?"

"Well, we were going out that way (toward West Side Junior High School) to see my friends. And we saw this fight so we got into it to help the white boys." He had not seen the start of it, he admitted, but he *knew* these white boys were walking along the sidewalk and these Negro boys came up to them and one Negro tried to grab a white boy's football cleat so the white boy hit him.

"Then the white boy really started the fight, didn't he?"

"But it was in self-defense." A long pause as he reconsidered the trend of his story. "So there was a bad fight and several of us got hurt." He bore no evidence of injury on face or hands. "And this sort of thing is gonna happen all the time."

I asked him his name. "Mike," he said. He had been in the 9th grade but he stopped school because he didn't like the system.

"What do you mean by that, the system?"

"Just the system," he repeated and thought a bit. "I couldn't learn anything."

I smiled at him. "You look like a mighty bright boy to me," and his eyes lighted as he said, "Oh, I'll get an education in the Navy."

"But you should be in school now," I protested and I suppose he lied, "Well, I'm studying art in the Arcade Building."

My brother listened with a pinched smile on his face. When Mike left, I asked, "Does it say anything to you about why I had to do what I'm doing?"

I had heard not a word from my brother or sister since the first announcement of the WEC. I knew they did not feel as I did about the racial problems but I had somehow expected family support.* My sister, Julia, and her husband, Pat, had driven from their retirement home in California to visit us before I knew what I must do. Their stay with my brother was to terminate on Friday, the 26th, but I told him a little of the disturbance of our home life and suggested that Julia and Pat stay with him and his wife until after the election. I was hurt that it was only a business matter which had brought him to our WEC office to see me and I told him so. He stared at me in silence, and I still wish I could have known his thoughts. Through the months to follow, although it was obvious that he did not share my social philosophy, I felt he assuaged his own conscience with generous donations to the WEC, and I was inestimably glad that my position did not hurt him, his family, or his business.

On the Saturday night before my vita was to appear in the *Gazette* on Sunday, September 21st, I called Bill Lewis and asked if he could possibly eliminate my maiden name and reference to my family. I had not heard a word from my brother or my sister and I was worried. Bill was sympathetic and said he

---

*My niece and her husband, Patricia and Skipper Rostker of Pasadena, California, upon hearing of the WEC, immediately sent me a wire: "We are proud of you."

would ask but he soon phoned back to say this was impossible because of my father's leadership in Little Rock. I bowed to this decision and prayed that any reprisals might be visited on me. They were.

Election day was a frenzied day, but if I had known more, I doubt that I could have done more. Nor could anyone else. The women had worked willingly, brilliantly, and I had a sublime optimism. I just could not believe that anyone would vote to have no schools. About noon, Ed Lester called me to suggest, "This is what you might say tonight."

Listening, I exclaimed, "But that is if we lose. What do I say if we win?" I'm grateful that he didn't laugh.

The morning of this election day, a Negro man, his wife and two children paraded in front of Hall High School with a sign reading, "Please vote for integration to help us have equality." Newspapers had been alerted and photographers were there. By 11:30 the *Arkansas Democrat* had the picture on the streets for voters to see as they headed toward the polls. The *Arkansas Gazette* later disclosed that the picture was staged, that the affair had been arranged by a friend of the Governor, but by then the voting was over. The count was 7,561 for integration and 19,470 against. Thus, Little Rock chose to close its four high schools (the all-white Central, Hall and Technical, and the all-Negro Horace Mann) to 3600 students rather than admit six Negroes to Central High School.

Dr. and Mrs. Morris asked Velma and Jay Powell, Joe and me to have dinner with them that evening, and it was from their home that I phoned the *Ga-*

zette to read to Bill Lewis the words which Ed Lester had written for me. This was the one, and only time anyone wrote a statement for me, but there were to be many times in the next two years that I wished for a ghost writer. Ed's statement was:

> It has become apparent that the voters of the Little Rock School District have chosen to take the fateful step of abandoning four public high schools. Naturally, we are disappointed with the results, for our Committee feels deeply that our community could ill afford to abandon free public education. We have lost an election, but all of us have the deep satisfaction of having stood up for what seemed right in our hearts. Our dedication to the principle of free public education remains unimpaired. Our group will, without recrimination or bitterness, continue to work for what we earnestly feel will be the ultimate victory for this principle.
>
> I want to express my personal appreciation to the women who worked so hard, gave so much and without complaint took all the abuse that was offered; and to the men without whose invaluable encouragement, advice and co-operation we could never have carried on our program.
>
> In saying goodnight, I ask all of our citizens to pray for better days for our community.

It is rather curious that I was not depressed by this lopsided vote. This was, I think, because of my satisfaction in being active and vocal, as I told Harry Ashmore when he thoughtfully phoned me the next night to assure me that I had handled everything "just right," and to wish us well. We had started something, and already three or four hundred women had expressed an eagerness to speak out. I was sure we would win in the end, and it was good to be on our way.

There was one sequel which brought to me the greatest compliment I have ever had. On the first evening my sister and her husband spent with us, the Sunday night following the election, Dan Wakefield of *The Nation* phoned, asking if he might drive out to see me. Not only was I wary of this sort of intrusion on my attempt to heal family relationships, but I was not at all sure it wouldn't be a further waste of time and effort. His friendly voice and his understanding manner won me, however, and I promised I would meet him the next day at my brother's office. We had a pleasant, even cordial conversation but I was not prepared for the October 11 issue of his magazine in which the lead article was "Siege at Little Rock." It read in part:

> The president of the committee, Mrs. Joe Brewer, is a Little Rock born and raised citizen and Smith College graduate who seems to embody the kind of dignity and grace that is the South at its best and is now its greatest hope. Faubus is Snopes and his kin are the majority; Mrs. Brewer and others like her, who are people of intelligence and principle, will always be, by nature, his greatest menace. A few days after the sad results of the voting, Mrs. Brewer explained to a visitor that "People have asked me if I wasn't despondent, but I'm really not — I'm glad about the response we

got. I don't know how many women worked with us finally but I personally talked to 250 and they all talked to others. And anyone who got involved with the committee knew there would be abusive letters and phone calls, and that their husbands might be hurt in business. There's a lot of fear and hate here, and there's apathy, too — so many people say there's just nothing you can do about it. But we're going to continue to do everything we can. At least we've made a start now and I'm sure we have a future. There are too many decent people here." Mrs. Brewer said that in the short time since the committee had been formed, "So many people have asked me — 'Why didn't you get started a year ago?' Well, we should have. But when it first happened we were numb. And I guess we were afraid."

Many of Little Rock's leaders are still either numb or afraid or both, and this was the Women's Emergency Committee's job, to prove that public education was more important than immobility and fear.

Three

A Second Crisis

In part to save our diminished funds, but also to avoid hecklers, we relinquished our office space and I began a peripatetic existence from home to home, from pay phone booth to pay phone booth. I soon knew the location of the majority of pay booths in Little Rock, in North Little Rock, and in the county between the city limits and our home. Even pay booths became suspect, however, for sometimes I could hear whispers or faint music on the wires, so I tried not to use the same one many times in succession. It was not that I always had such valuable secrets to impart but that I did not want to identify the person to whom I talked. When women, or their husbands, became convinced that their home phones had been tapped, I ceased going to their homes or calling them there. I tried very hard to spare every woman the resulting harassment her suspected stand for public education would surely bring her.

I worked long hours with Velma Powell's help at the Arkansas Council on Human Relations until I narrowly escaped being caught there when Attorney General Bruce Bennett, stirring more hatred by accusing the Council of being communists, sent police to the door during a routine meeting. This caused two male members of the Council board to dash out the back door and hurdle the back fence. I was grateful to have escaped such an exit.

In those hectic days, I was assembling data and making plans for the next meeting of the WEC. As early as our first meeting, we had set the date and place — October 7 at the Terry home — for this meeting. I found our women as determined as I.

Three thousand six hundred and ninety-eight students were displaced persons, we were told, and many of them were not in schools anywhere. The YWCA had started classes in French. There were TV lessons early each morning. Pulaski County had absorbed 247 Little Rock students. Some parents had rented apartments in North Little Rock so their children could attend that high school. Some parents, in despair, had sent their children out of the state, to live with relatives or friends, or to attend private schools. Some families were moving away permanently. Trinity Episcopal Cathedral and the Second Baptist Church had announced plans to open high schools. Faubus' Private School Corporation was still trying to use the public high school to house its segregated school. Suits flew in and out of courts, confusing everyone.

In February, 1959, the testimony of the Superintendent of Little Rock schools in Federal Court indicated that 3,665 high school students were locked out of their public schools. Of these, 2,915 white students were divided: 1,120 in private schools at Little Rock and Conway, 877 in other public schools in Arkansas, 275 attending schools outside the state, and 643 not in any school. Of the 750 Negro students, 229 were in public schools elsewhere in Arkansas, 79 were in schools outside the state and 442 were not in school.

The teachers and staffs in the high schools, about 175 persons, were as bewildered as the parents. The attorney for the Classroom Teachers Association had advised them not to teach in the private school corporation school. Those under contract were still being paid (some $19,000 per week to the teachers under contract, exclusive of several thousand dollars of fixed overhead and debt service for the four empty high schools) but they sat in empty classrooms. A few managed to do substitute teaching in the elementary and junior high schools. Eventually the studentless ones formed classes among themselves; classes in English, Spanish, French and German; in typing, and speech; in ceramics, art, photography; in sewing; in square dancing; — teaching each other individual specialties. Some teachers wrote curriculum guides in various subjects. But the days were long and the future was a big question mark.

Facing this malaise, the WEC was eager for activity. We began by writing letters to anyone who had been courageous enough to speak, circulating among ourselves lists of the names and addresses of the sixty-three attorneys who had signed the protesting advertisement in September, of the ministers who had appeared on our TV shows or had made public statements, and of contributors who had said, "You may use my name if you want to." We also supplied lists of our Senators and Congressmen, asking the women to urge their support of our public schools.

We formed committees: policy, membership, program, projects, publicity, finance. We retained the steering committee, and these attractive young women often delivered materials personally to the silent men of our town. We set up a small executive committee which would meet weekly to keep our momentum between the monthly meetings of the larger organization. Jane Mendel agreed to set up a telephone chain, and she performed a miracle, grouping the women under captains and sub-captains so that our entire mailing list, even as it grew to 1,000 and more, could be reached within a few hours. We organized a night group, to carry word of our activities and plans to working women who could not attend our afternoon session. A brave teacher, Mrs. H.H. Hunt, agreed to chair this session. We asked a committee to visit the high school teachers, to lunch with them, to attempt to buoy their morale.

But probably the most memorable item on this day's agenda was a letter to our governor. He had remarked publicly that he was not ready to retreat from the impasse with the government, that none of his legal advisers or "anyone else" was urging him to do so. This inferred that no one had really asked him to re-open the schools and certainly this was what we thought we had been saying loud and clear. This was our letter; the only direct communication between us in the five year history of the WEC:

The Honorable Orval E. Faubus
Governor of Arkansas
State Capitol
Little Rock, Arkansas

Dear Governor Faubus:

The Women's Emergency Committee to Open Our Schools met today (Tuesday, October 7) at 1:30 and unanimously passed a resolution to affirm its dedication to the principle of free public education, and to so advise you.

We, the Women's Emergency Committee, deplore the closing of our four public high schools, feel deeply that this can only impair the reputation, the development and even peace of our city, our state and our country.

Wherefore, we respectfully urge you to take any and all necessary steps to reopen our four free public high schools immediately.

Sincerely,

Mrs. Joe R. Brewer
Chairman
Mrs. Woodbridge Morris
Secretary

We gave copies of this to the local papers. We had no answer, and heard no comment from Mr. Faubus.

When the Private School Corporation was unable to lease the public school facilities — as the Federal Appeals Court enjoined the Little Rock School Board from this course — it sent out an urgent request for funds which brought in donations from across the South. It then leased the building formerly used by the University of Arkansas Graduate Center which had been bought the week before by a private citizen for a reported $50,000.00. On October 22, Faubus announced that $3,000 to $4,000 was coming in daily for the private school which was to be known as the T.J. Raney High School, and some 231 seniors, 241 juniors and about 240 sophomores had already registered; that fourteen teachers, a principal and two secretaries had been hired. By then the Baptist High School also had registered 343 students and was searching for more teachers. The teacher problem plagued all of these burgeoning private schools, and Faubus blamed the Little Rock School Board, one of his whipping boys, for not releasing the public school teachers. Any thinking person knew that at best these schools could be only stop-gap solutions, with limited staffs, inadequate equipment and insufficient libraries. I was appalled to learn the names of many supporters of the Raney School.

One attorney suggested a possible method of solving our dilemma. Could we find parents of high school students who would be willing to file a suit against the school board, claiming they were discriminated against under the Arkansas Constitution which guaranteed an education to all children between the ages of six and eighteen, and at the same time asking for an injunction against the governor from interfering with the opening of the schools? Although there was a law on our books against barratry, and I was recklessly running the risk of being accused under it, I spent hours in pay booths talking with persons whose names were given to me but whose faces I never saw. Twice I thought we had found the brave ones we needed, but in both cases the families moved out of the School district before details could be worked out. The suit was never filed.

Quite thoughtlessly, I ran another risk. In mid October, Dr. Dale Alford, the segregationist member of the Little Rock School Board, announced that he had been approached to run as a write-in candidate for the United States Congress against Representative Brooks Hays. On November 2, the Attorney General of Arkansas ruled that paste-in stickers for Alford were quite legal and on November 4, at the same election in which Faubus defeated Jim Johnson to win his third term as governor, Dale Alford defeated Brooks Hays by a vote of 30,739 to 29,483 for the Fifth District seat in the U.S. House of Representatives. Soon after this election, I had occasion to call on Brooks Hays in his office in the federal building in Little Rock and I was shocked to realize what a crushing blow his defeat had been. I hope subsequent honors and appointments may have obliterated his memory of those days.

A number of our women reported illegalities in this election and we decided to document them and report them to Washington. This was a fruitless protest. I quote the *Arkansas Democrat*, June 19, 1959:

> After a long probe of the Alford-Hays election last November, which gave Representative Alford a lead of about 1200 votes, a Federal grand jury's find is "No true bill to be reported." This means the jury saw no violation of federal law, or at least uncovered no evidence of violation sufficient to support an indictment. The Grand Jury, in three months plus, looked into a cross section of ballot boxes in the Fifth District, gave everyone who had a complaint a chance to testify, and weighed an FBI report.

My energies were being depleted with constant driving to conferences in all parts of the city, and I was spending unbelievable amounts of my own nickels in phone booths. Worst of all, it was extremely difficult to co-ordinate activities, despite the dedication of the executive committee and the generous use of Mrs. Terry's home. At our November 4 general meeting, an appeal was made for the use of a room, a garage — any space we could call a central office where we could stack material, house a lending library, and merge the various facets of our program. Dr. and Mrs. Payton Kolb, living at 224

Colonial Court, came to our rescue. They offered a room which was separate from, although a part of, their home, a room which had an outside entrance to the rear garden. There was a small powder room adjoining it. If necessary, we could use this space until the following June, when a relative would occupy it for the summer. We had only to install our phone, an unlisted one in the name of the WEC. We would, of course, pay the nominal utility bills.

Immediately we set up a list of volunteers to staff the new office beginning Monday, November 10, and we urged all typists to give us some time, day or night. Who could loan us a typewriter? A small file case? Who knew of a mimeograph machine we could use, day, night, or weekends?

On November 2, we had issued the first of a long series of flyers urging the reopening of our schools. We had accumulated lists of PTA memberships, Chamber of Commerce members, lists of men's and women's service clubs. We planned to bombard thousands of citizens with our conviction that we *must* have public education. This first sheet was a more finished product than we ever again felt wealthy enough to produce. It was in bold print on a good grade of paper:

WHERE IS OUR PRIDE!
MAKE SHIFT SCHOOLS WON'T DO!

Three of the best high schools in the country stand empty; the teachers wait for their classes; our children are locked out! We substitute inadequate, make shift schools and send begging letters all over the United States, asking for money. Where is our intelligence?

WHERE IS OUR PRIDE?
WHERE ARE WE GOING?
WHAT IS THE PLAN?

Will school closings stop with the Little Rock high schools? Is the next step to close all Arkansas public schools? The Governor's Committee on Education has already told us that Arkansas' schools are inadequate. Make shift schools can't raise their standards — but will cost more! **WHERE ARE WE GOING!**

Will you gamble your child's birthright on a pig in a poke?

OUR CHILDREN CAN'T WAIT FOREVER — LET'S OPEN OUR SCHOOLS

THE WOMEN'S EMERGENCY COMMITTEE TO OPEN OUR SCHOOLS

When I entered our new office in the Kolb home on Monday, November 10, a young woman whom I did not know interrupted my approach to my desk. "I am Irene Samuel," she said. "I have had training in organizational work and I am willing to devote my entire time to running this office. My experience —" I stopped her recitation of federal form 57 to say, "I couldn't be happier to see you." To have someone eager to take over the details of the office, on a full time schedule, seemed more than I could have hoped for.

Irene's husband, Dr. John Samuel, was a successful doctor and a member of the Academy of General Practice. Both were natives of Little Rock and graduates of its public schools. Their son, Lou, was then about eight years old. Before her marriage and during her husband's service overseas, she had been employed in Washington, D.C. in public administration. She proved to be a master of detail, turning out work with great rapidity, and she expected everyone else to match her pace. The office hummed with activity.

Now, I was able to spend my time on policy, on interviews both in and out of the office, on composition of materials. In a year I literally wore out a leather brief case, carrying it every place I went, always stuffed with leaflets, my note and date book, scratch paper, reading material, letters, whatever. I acquired a habit of keeping a legal size pad and a pencil on the car seat beside me as I drove to and from town, and at stop lights I jotted down notes, drafted letters and worked out forms.

I spent much time trying to see business men who were far from eager to see me. I choose one episode as typical. I had known a prominent banker for some years. He had been popular politically in Little Rock and had become increasingly influential in the business world. If he would take the lead, I felt sure he could break through the wall of silence with which the men in Little Rock surrounded themselves. I went to see him several times but he was never "in." I called him by telephone but was never able to reach him. Finally, I had the luck to meet him on the street as he rounded a corner and could not escape me. "No, I'm not going to get into this," he said crossly. "I've pulled Little Rock's chestnuts out of the fire time after time and I'm tired of it. Besides it is not going to hurt anybody for those schools to stay closed for a year. My son had to miss two years of school when he went in the service and it didn't hurt him. You women ought to leave this thing alone. You are the ones stirring up trouble." It made me ill to listen to him, a successful, intelligent man. How guilty he must feel, I thought. Although I saw him often as I crossed the bank lobby in the ensuing months, it was nearly two years before he "saw" me again.

In early November, the Council on Education, the policy setting body of the Arkansas Education Association (A.E.A.), pledged its efforts to preserve the public school system and recommended a county-by-county method of keeping watch on the state legislature. Their statement was a mild one, but the Arkansas Legislative Council, obviously angered, delayed consideration of the Education Department budget, and implied they might reduce state aid to the schools. Following our resolve to miss no opportunity to speak out, the WEC sent a telegram to Forrest Rozzell, the executive secretary of the A.E.A., and submitted a copy of it to the papers. The committee said:

> The Women's Emergency Committee to Open Our
> Schools expresses complete agreement with the
> A.E.A. pledge to work to preserve our free public
> education. We want to assure you of our desire to
> work with you in any way we can. We are deeply
> gratified that the teachers of our state share our
> concern over the future of our schools.
>
> We believe that public school education is threat-
> ened in all of Arkansas unless it is preserved at
> Little Rock. Our committee, therefore, is urging
> that Little Rock high schools be opened now.
>
> We believe that other citizens of the state as well
> as of our community share this concern and will
> join our efforts to preserve our free public educa-
> tion.

On November 26, we quite lost our tempers.
Claude Carpenter, Jr., executive secretary to Governor Faubus and state chairman of the Democratic
Party fund campaign, solicited $5.00 each from the
14,698 public school teachers and administrators
as an expression of their appreciation to Governor
Faubus for the things he had done for them! Again
the WEC had an item for the newspapers as we sent
the identical wire to Mr. Paul Butler, Democratic National Committee chairman in Washington, D.C., to
Mr. Claude D. Carpenter, Jr., and to Mr. Tom Harper,
chairman of the state Democratic Committee, Fort
Smith, Arkansas:

> We protest the pressure being brought to bear on
> the Arkansas teachers by the "Dollars for Demo-
> crats" Fund Drive. We feel this is contrary to the
> high principles of the Democratic party.

There was no answer and no retraction but the matter was quietly dropped, and Governor Faubus was reported to have remarked when asked about Mr. Carpenter's letter that he wouldn't have done it "just that way."

Meanwhile, the state Board of Education had figured that the Little Rock high school students could receive $172.66 each as the individual share of the state aid withheld. On November 17, the Department began making payments of $24.50 per month per student to other schools for educating these displaced students, under the authority of Act 5 of 1958; and they continued to do so until March 8, 1959, when the U.S. District Court enjoined the state from paying out Little Rock District funds. In January of 1959, the state gave a grade A accreditation to the private T.J. Raney High School. As chairman of the WEC, I wired Mr. Arch Ford, Arkansas Education Department, State Capitol:

> Our 1,024 members request you withhold payment of any state funds to Raney High School or any other private school until validity of the acts under which such payments are contemplated has been determined by our state courts. To expend the state funds under a doubtful procedure may result in an irretrievable loss of school funds.

There was no answer and Raney High received $71,907.50 of the Little Rock funds before Act 5 was declared unconstitutional. Of the $510,220 funds withheld for 1958-59, the state Board of Education also paid out $76,317.50 to the Pulaski County Rural School District, $3,993.50 to the town of Hazen,

Arkansas and $1,984.50 to the city of Hot Springs. None of this was ever repaid and this was a source of bitter discussion at every executive committee meeting of the WEC. We felt utterly frustrated that we could think of nothing to do about it. We wanted to file a suit but the advice of attorneys was that such action would be all but hopeless and might only stir up more trouble, more worries for us.

If we felt frustrated, the Little Rock School Board felt defeated. Under instructions to integrate the schools with all deliberate speed, the board was blocked by the governor's school closing order. When the board proceeded to cancel football and band practice, Mr. Faubus rebuked them sternly and the board reinstated these two extracurricular activities. The board petitioned the Federal Court for a decision on whether it could legally lease the public school buildings to the private school corporation. Judge John E. Miller declined to take this petition under advisement. "I have no inclination to shirk my responsibilities," he opined, "but this Court is without authority to rule on the matter before it." While the NAACP appealed this case, the Little Rock School Board leased the closed high school to the private school corporation and within hours was enjoined from going through with the transaction. Faubus then blamed the board for not releasing the teachers and the board said it would release any who asked to transfer; however the Court enjoined the teachers from transferring to the private schools. Finally, on November 10, the three judge panel of the 8th Circuit Court issued a permanent injunction against the use of public buildings by a private school, and ordered Judge Miller and Little Rock School Board to take positive steps to integrate. On November 12, exasperated, "hopeless and helpless," the school board bought out Virgil Blossom's contract as superintendent of the Little Rock schools and resigned. The WEC was dismayed by this development and tried in vain to persuade the five members of the school board (all except Dr. Dale Alford) to reconsider.

Thus we were faced with a city with no school board. The school board election was set for December 6 and this meant that all candidates must file by Saturday, November 15. As of November 14, the only announced slate of candidates was that headed by James Karam, Little Rock business man and "crony of Governor Faubus," an arch critic of the School Board. Evidence of Karam's interest in being on the board was contained in his announcement that if elected, he would return Superintendent Blossom as assistant principal at a Negro school.

We had three days to find six candidates who believed in public education and to get each petition for candidacy signed by at least twenty-five qualified voters. Once more we hungered for action from the men of our town. Why could not the bankers find strength in togetherness and produce a slate? There was no report to reassure us. Friday afternoon, the 14th, Grainger Williams, president of the Chamber of Commerce, whose wife was a loyal member of the WEC, met with our officers, told us of the failure of the business men to produce a slate and left with us a list of names of prospects we might try to induce to run. We learned that Ted Lamb had come forward of his own volition, shocked by the dearth of opposition to Jimmy Karam, but where would we find five more dedicated souls?

In the middle of this tension, my husband had word of the death of a relative and we were out of town on that fateful Saturday. Driving back late that night, I stopped in a booth and talked with Mrs. Terry. She had had a hectic 24 hours. Taking in hand the list Grainger Williams had left with us, she had spent the most of Friday evening calling one name after another. She had four yeses when she reached the last name as it neared midnight. One more yes was all she needed because Billy Rector had agreed to run if Ed McKinley, in sixth place, had no opposition. The other interested men had bought this. Russell Matson was in Fayetteville for a football game, she found, so she promptly telephoned him there, and to her relief heard, "Yes, I'll run but I won't be home until tomorrow night."

"We'll manage somehow," Adolphine assured him, "to file for you." Ever resourceful, under the exigency of the moment, she simply forged his name at the Court House to hold his candidacy over the 6 p.m. deadline until he arrived back in Little Rock that evening and signed his own autograph. All day, several of our women had scurried over town getting the five petitions properly signed, and by six o'clock, we had a "business man's slate."

Before I left the pay booth, I phoned Bob Shults. "Why did they have no one oppose Ed McKinley?" he wanted to know. I wanted to know, too, for the supposed reasoning that a slate of five would be psychologically more effective than a slate of six had no logic in it for me, and I could not forget that at the time one of the school board members had resigned in mid-September, it had been Ed McKinley whom Dr. Dale Alford had wanted to elect in his place. But the die was cast, time had run out, and I felt optimistic that we had some good candidates to support.

Our own Margaret Stephens (Mrs. Charles W.) had agreed to run and had drawn Position II for a two year term against R.W. (Bob) Laster, our municipal judge and a viciously vocal segregationist. Ted Lamb, of the public relations firm which had helped us fight the September 27 election, a known liberal who was to stand alone through years of conflict with a conservative board, was opposed by Dr. George P. Branscum and Mrs. Pauline Woodson, a member of the screaming Mothers League. Russell H. Matson, Jr., whom two of our executive board interviewed and reported on most favorably as "our golden boy," would face C.C. Railey. W.F. (Billy) Rector, a highly successful businessman with widespread connections in real estate, insurance and brokerage firms, opposed Ben D. Rowland, Sr. Everett Tucker, Jr., the manager of the Industrial Development Company in Little Rock and owner and manager of a family plantation at Tucker, Arkansas, would face John W. Clayton, something of an unknown, and Mrs. Margaret Morrison, another leader of the Mothers League. James Karam had withdrawn as of November 16. We had a big job ahead of us.

Billy Rector appointed himself spokesman for "our" slate and came to our office to confer on plans. He was decisively abrupt, almost belligerent, and I tried to smooth our paths a bit by telling him I had known some of his family in my banking days and that my father had spoken of him as a most promising young man. It was obvious that this mattered not one whit to him. He had no time for pleasantries. He wanted total efforts of our organization on behalf of "his" slate but he made it clear that no one should know of our alliance. "Now this is what you do and this is the way you do it" were his instructions.

I decided to talk with Ted Lamb about their advertising. "We are going to work our heads off for you," I promised, "but we insist you don't lay it on too thick about being segregationists. I know your problems, but we're not going to rouse much enthusiasm for you if you sound like the White Citizens Council." He couldn't have agreed more and he did all he could. Although Faubus had made his usual accusation that the "business man's slate" was made up of integrationists, Billy Rector's attempt to counteract this by an announcement that he had given $100.00 to the Capital Citizens Council in 1957 for a lawsuit did not cheer us.

We had agreed we must not back this slate as a committee, indeed they had asked us not to, but we urged everyone on our mailing list to support our five in every way possible. Captains were appointed for each ward to head committees to distribute cards, to address cards for mailing, to telephone, to supply cars to the polls. We had an effective organization involving well over 600 women and they put their hearts into this critical campaign. At home, my phone calls increased in frequency and abusiveness, which seemed a good sign. The vote of December 6th elected Ted Lamb for a three-year term, Russell Matson for two years and Everett Tucker for one year. We had every faith we could depend on them; but the unopposed Ed McKinley, and the successful Ben Rowland and Bob Laster, indicated their intention to co-operate with the governor. It was only days until Ed McKinley was elected to the board of the Private School Corporation. So here we were, we realized soberly, three against three.

Four

COYA, Come Home

The pressures increased with each day of closed schools. We were, by November, sending out some 2500 flyers each week. Always with an eagerness to share in our efforts, members came in and out of our office constantly, often with small children tugging at their skirts, often with babies in their arms. Many took boxes of envelopes home to address, stuff and stamp. Some developed a delivery service, taking tasks to shut-ins who wanted to have a part in our work. Some did the mimeographing in various places where we had sympathetic friends: the Arkansas Council on Human Relations; a few churches; even in one of the closed schools. Many women worked on into the night. I brought projects home as the day waned for Joe objected to my driving out from town after dark, and he worried the many evenings I reached home at fading twilight.

Occasionally the mailed flyers were returned with a contribution. Sometimes they were returned to us with insulting remarks:

"I've not the slightest interest in your filthy propaganda. Just what is your answer — rape, knifing, murder, etc., like Detroit, Washington, New York? Why don't you sit down and *think?*"

Or, simply, "Please take me off your mailing list." In any case, we felt this particular flyer must have hit the target.

We endeavored to keep all of them on a dignified plane, and confined to intelligent argument. This is a sample:

THE GOVERNOR'S ADVISORY COMMITTEE ON EDUCATION (GACE)*

believes...

"The public school system of the state is the cornerstone of our social, economic, and political structure and should, therefore, be the concern of all citizens.

"There is a direct relationship between the success of Arkansas' program of industrial development and the promptness and adequacy of the solution to our educational problems."

and agrees with the U.S. Chamber of Commerce that...

"GOOD SCHOOLS ARE GOOD BUSINESS"

---

* A non-political study group of 58 business and school leaders throughout Arkansas. Little Rock members: Virgil Blossom, J.R. Booker, Claude Carpenter, Jr., LeRay

One flyer taught us a lesson. Our artists blocked out four little houses under the heading *Brotherhood Week*, each one labeled with the name of one of the four high schools and marked "closed." Under this was stenciled: "The world is now too dangerous for anything but the TRUTH, too small for anything but BROTHERHOOD." We signed this as a quote from Adlai Stevenson above the WEC signature and address. We turned this draft over to those who mimeographed and arranged for mailing, but when the flyers poured back to us the next week from angry and frightened addressees in excited protest, we saw that someone on our staff had thought the drawing not quite explicit enough for the text and had added outstretched hands between the houses joining the three all white high schools to the one all black high school. This was all that was needed to bring on another barrage of "Integrationists!" From then on, we carefully screened every drawing not only when first presented but also after it was stenciled, and we checked every set of flyers before mailing.

It became more and more obvious that we needed to clarify our position to the public in a formal statement. A policy committee submitted a work sheet

---

Cristophe, A.W. Ford, Mrs. Charles R. Henry, Lewis Johnson, Mrs. Frances Neal, Hugh B. Patterson, Jr. , H.R. Pyle, Forrest Rozzell, Joshua K. Shepherd, B.G. Williams, Mrs. Edgar F. Dixon.

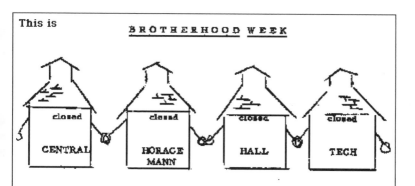

WEC "Brotherhood Week" mailing

THE

    MAN

        WHO

            THINKS

                FOR

                    HIMSELF

                        WANTS FREE PUBLIC SCHOOLS!

Americans take pride in being able
to think for themselves and in being
able to say what they think.

WHAT DO YOU WANT?

LITTLE ROCK PUBLIC SCHOOLS HAVE . . .

        Libraries
        Laboratories for scientific training
        Vocational training shops
        Well-rounded sports programs
        Bands
        Special activities such as news-
          papers, drama, music, debating
        And, a wide selection of courses

SAYING WHAT YOU THINK IS AS IMPORTANT AS THINKING IT!

    SPEAK OUT FOR PUBLIC SCHOOLS!

Women's Emergency Committee To Open Our Schools

WEC mailings

EVERY CHILD HAS THE RIGHT . . .

"The State shall ever maintain

A GENERAL, SUITABLE AND EFFICIENT

S Y S T E M O F F R E E S C H O O L S

whereby all persons in the State

between the ages of

six and twenty-one years

may receive

gratuitous instruction."   Article 14

Constitution of the State of Arkansas.

WILL YOURS ?

LET'S OPEN OUR PUBLIC SCHOOLS -- AND KEEP THEM OPEN !

Women's Emergency Committee To Open Our Schools

DON'T

HIDE

FROM

THE

FACTS!!

LITTLE

ROCK

IS

SPENDING:

MORE THAN $1,000,000.00 FOR CLOSED SCHOOLS
PLUS HUNDREDS OF THOUSANDS OF $$$ FOR MAKESHIFT SCHOOLING

To get the BEST JOB your CHILD needs the BEST SCHOOLS

Let's have the best schools for the most children FREE PUBLIC SCHOOLS

The Women's Emergency Committee To Open Our Schools

and after much discussion, many suggestions and revisions, the executive committee produced a dignified page which we distributed widely:

THE WOMEN'S EMERGENCY COMMITTEE TO OPEN OUR SCHOOLS

Policy & Purpose

The Women's Emergency Committee to Open Our Schools is dedicated to the principle of free public school education, and to law and order. We stand neither for integration nor for segregation, but for education.

OUR AIM IS:
to get the four free public high schools reopened; to get the students back in their classes; to retain our staff of good teachers; to regain full accreditation by the North Central Association.

We know that the "school situation" at Little Rock is not simply a local problem...and that Arkansas has been disgraced in the eyes of the entire world. We realize that what has happened here is elsewhere considered symbolic of "American Democracy" and so has made every American Citizen the object of distrust and even hate.

We believe that our free public school system is essential to the future of our city and state.

It is our hope to say to the world that there are many of us here who care enough to do something about this problem.

This was the most formal facet of our organization during these frenetic months. We had no constitution, no by-laws. I was all too vague on the question of procedure and Roberts Rules of Order, for I had avoided clubs all my life, but if anyone minded the informality of our meetings, I never knew it. We were all too intent on the business at hand to care whether Mrs. X's suggestion was a motion or a point of discussion. I believed in hearing every idea, tossing it to our group, discarding it or developing it into a decisive plan. We moved together with a remarkable rapport.

During this concentration on school activities and office detail, Mrs. Terry, Mrs. Powell and I had been thinking constantly of the racial problem. We early realized that if the WEC were to accomplish the purpose expressed in its name, it was imperative that we adhere strictly to that purpose. To do so, we could not openly involve ourselves in any inter-racial associations. To combat the hysterical foes of integration we must defeat them and their proposals at the polls. To amass a vote assuring such defeat in our nightmare atmosphere of racial prejudice, we must not, in any way, give any basis for the constantly repeated accusation that we were integrationists. Over and over we proclaimed: "We stand neither for integration nor for segregation, but for education." It would be suicide to accept Negro women as members. It would be fatal to be seen at a meeting of Negroes. It was dangerous to visit the Arkansas Council on Human Relations.

This policy was and is difficult to explain to liberals who did not or do not understand our situation in those years. Even I can now wonder that our city and state could have been so completely obsessed with an emotional racial trauma. There was little doubt that ignorance played a big part in it and, intent on gaining an unprecedented tenure of office (six terms, alas), the governor repeatedly agitated this neurosis. The continuing attempts to pass laws which would destroy public schools, and the ardent efforts to elect segregationist school board members, city directors, and state legislators, made it apparent that our sharpest weapon was the vote. The integrationist vote was a feeble minority. The Negro vote was small and uninformed. If we accepted or tolerated a single hint of favoring integration, we were a lost cause. For many months, in our executive board meetings, we faced this issue. Over and over, depressed but realistic, we decided against inviting Negro members, against attending inter-racial groups.

From time to time I made cautiously private phone calls to Negro leaders assuring them of our concern, and explaining the WEC's limitation to white female membership. Secretly I talked with women in the Phyllis Wheatley YWCA (Negro), and I called teachers in the Horace Mann High School (Negro) and in the Arkansas Teachers Association (Negro) hoping they believed in my sincerity and explained our reasoning to their friends. But not all Negroes understood. Years later, Mrs. Daisy Bates told me that she had written a long article blasting our committee because we were working *for* the Negroes, not

71

with them, but she put it away without publishing it in deference to Mrs. Terry whom she admired wholeheartedly.

There were more immediate indications of disapproval. Dr. Jack Massie, a noted Negro physician and a militant civil rights worker, called me and asked that I speak at a meeting of an integrated group, a small organization under the aegis of the Arkansas Council on Human Relations. Although I was still shy of speaking, I wanted desperately to say yes, but our executive committee thought this premature — and very dangerous. I had to tell him no, and I don't know why I didn't develop ulcers at the tone and words of his comment. It was all too obvious *he* did not understand our position.

During these fall months, Velma had been working on a proposal for a civic interracial committee. This, the policy committee decided, we might risk presenting as a preliminary move to calm the fears of our citizens. Although there were varying degrees of liberalism and conservatism within our executive committee, all of these women recognized the need for and the value of such a civic organization. Together we prepared a plan and it became my obligation to get this before the city directors. Trying to lay the groundwork, I phoned them one by one for appointments. In turn I reached only the secretaries or I had a response similar to that of then Mayor Werner C. Knoop. "There is no reason for you to come to my office. There is no reason for you to talk with me. If this comes up before the directors, we will consider it in due course." That he was to tour the world with a group of mayors not long after this bothered me. How would he be explaining "Little Rock"?

I went to see Mrs. Edgar F. Dixon, the one woman on the Board of City Directors, a woman sympathetic to our committee. She saw no problem. "Of course," she advised. "Go ahead and present it. They are all fine men. I know they will approve." This was to be a sad lesson in communication. I should have spent months, if necessary, to convince the city directors singly. Instead we gave them the opportunity to rebuff us. On December 19, we sent a letter to the Board of Directors of Little Rock, including a list of suggestions for the organization of an inter-racial commission, and we directed copies to Warren E. Bray of the Board of Directors of the Chamber of Commerce, and to Dean Dauley, the City Manager. The body of the letter read:

> We are especially grateful that Little Rock has a splendid organization of its city government and that the personnel recognizes its responsibilities in the continually deteriorating situation in our city.
>
> We are sure you are aware of the fear and hatred prevalent in our city. Therefore, we respectfully offer this suggestion: that there be formed a City Commission or Committee on Civic Unity, representative of all groups in our city, to provide or help build a climate of public opinion to support healthy and peaceful human relations.
>
> For your consideration, there is attached hereto a proposed outline of the creation and functions of such a commission.
>
> Through this commission, all community leaders and organizations might be stimulated to join in a movement to regain community solidarity.

The enclosure was this:

SUGGESTIONS FOR A COMMISSION ON CIVIC UNITY

<u>Purpose</u> of such a commission might be:

1. to promote community relations within the City and to foster the good name of Little Rock.

2. to cultivate understanding and friendly relations between all the various segments of population in the City of Little Rock.

<u>An Ordinance</u> might empower such a commission to:

1. Cooperate with other governmental and community agencies (both public and private) in programs to increase understanding and good will among the citizens of the community.

2. Serve in an advisory capacity to the city government, the school board, and various other agencies to make specific suggestions which might help solve the problems of law observance and enforcement, health, education, diminishing juvenile delinquency, etc.

Other points to be considered:

The commission should be truly representative of the city's population, should include members from all areas of society, should be inter-faith, inter-racial. Appointments to the commission might be made by having various groups, agencies and organizations submit a list of three or four persons to the City Board of Directors from which one or perhaps two would be appointed to the commission. These might include such groups as:

Chamber of Commerce

Ministerial Association

United Church Women

Youth Coordination Committee of Community Council

Business and Professional Women's Club

Temple B'Nai Israel

Congregation Agudath Achim

Religion and Labor Group

PTA Council — white

PTA Council — Negro

A labor group

Catholic Council of the Central Deanery

Knights of Columbus

Social Workers group

The Urban League

Women's Emergency

Ex-officio members from City Health Dept.,

Police Dept., etc.

A synopsis of this was carried by the papers and this publicity may have frightened these men. Mrs. Dixon's cohorts on the Little Rock Board of Directors, not as brave or as wise as she had thought, declined to act on our request for the appointment of a civic commission on unity. I have always felt this was one of my major mistakes. Preparation, careful preparation must be made for any controversial suggestion, mild and thoroughly supported by experience as it may be.*

* "Bishop Brown traced the organization to 1958, when a number of persons, primarily downtown businessmen, organized anonymously to try to end the strife that resulted from Governor Faubus' attempt to block court-ordered desegregation at Central High School." Somehow I could not take this silently and I wrote a letter that day to the editor of the *Arkansas Gazette* which was published in their *From the People* section under a headline:

THE LONG WAIT FOR CITY SUPPORT

It is interesting to learn, eight years late, that a number of persons, primarily downtown businessmen, organized informally and anonymously to try to end the strife that resulted from Governor Faubus' attempt to block court-ordered desegregation at Central High School.

It would have been vastly helpful to us, the women of the Women's Emergency Committee who were not anonymous, to have been aware of this anonymous organization.

Will it be remembered that in December of 1958 the Women's Emergency Committee tried — unsuccessfully, alas — to persuade the City Directors to sponsor an inter-faith, inter-racial commission on civic unity? We felt then that an interracial council, to be effective, deserved official status. I feel this is true today, and while I welcome the announcement of the Citizens Committee on Human Affairs, I hope we need not wait eight years longer to know it has the blessing of our city government.

Sincerely,

(sig) *Mrs. Joe R. Brewer*

As the year advanced with no hope of seeing the four schools reopened during the first term, we found it increasingly evident that the entire state educational program was in danger. We determined that we must try to reach a state-wide group. We directed a letter to every presumably concerned person whose name we could ascertain: officers of local branches of the University Women, of PTAs, of the League of Women Voters. It read:

WOMEN'S EMERGENCY COMMITTEE
TO
OPEN OUR SCHOOLS

The Women's Emergency Committee is a group which grew out of deep concern over Little Rock's closed high schools and the threat to all public schools. This committee is not affiliated with any other group in any way. It is composed of white women, primarily of Little Rock, with membership growing daily throughout Arkansas. We stand neither for integration nor for segregation, but for education.

We believe, and this is affirmed by attorneys, that under existing court orders, there are only two courses of action open to Little Rock:

1. Proceed toward minimum compliance with the court orders, or

2. Continue the destruction of the public school system. The latter alternative is unthinkable — a price we cannot afford to pay. If we are to build a better state

---

for ourselves and our children, we must provide free public school education for every child in Arkansas.

To preserve our public school system, the support of every thinking person is necessary. Whether or not you have children, whether or not your children are in public schools, whether or not you can be active, *WE NEED YOU!*

Please fill out and return the blank at the bottom of the page.

Sincerely yours,
(signed)   *Vivion L. Brewer*
Mrs. Joe R. Brewer, Chairman

I believe in the preservation of free public education and respect for law and order.

Signature _____

Address _____

Please mail with contribution to:
    PO Box 122, Pulaski Heights Station
    Little Rock, Arkansas

We had some gratifying responses and at our December 2nd general meeting, I was able to announce the expansion of our committee in five Arkansas towns: Fayetteville, Fort Smith, El Dorado, Paris and Eureka Springs.

From one of these sources came a new idea. One morning, about 8 o'clock, as I was getting ready to leave home, a friendly voice on a long distance line said, "I live in El Dorado. I am interested in what you are doing. I'd like to know more about you." The caller was gracious and tactful but she made me understand clearly that women who did not know me, indeed had never heard of me, needed to be reassured before becoming involved. I wondered why I had never thought of this before. Of course everyone wants to know something about the personnel of a group she considers joining. Since so much material concerning the WEC went out over my signature, I must be more than a name. Her call led to the writing of my profile. This sheet, which accompanied many letters sent out of the city, also included the names of the members of our executive committee, a valiant step forward in our publicity:

PROFILE OF MRS. BREWER

VIVION LENON BREWER (Mrs. Joe R. Brewer): Born and reared in Little Rock; daughter of W. E. Lenon, Little Rock mayor 1903-1908. Graduate of Little Rock High School, Smith College (Class of 1921), Arkansas Law School. Until marriage in 1930, vice president and director of People's Trust Company, Little Rock (the forerunner of the present First National Bank). From 1930 to 1946 lived in Washington, D.C., with her husband, a government career man who served in the Air Force during World War II. In 1946, returned to Arkansas where husband is personnel officer at the Veterans Administration Hospital, North Little Rock. Present home is the family's former recreation spot at Scott, Arkansas, 13 miles from downtown Little Rock. No children.

EXECUTIVE COMMITTEE, Women's Emergency Committee to Open Our Schools:

Mrs Joe R. Brewer, Mrs. Woodbridge Morris, Miss Ada May Smith, Mrs. D.D. Terry, Mrs. Harry S. Ashmore, Mrs. W.H. Thompson, Mrs. J.O. Powell, Mrs. Earl Cotton, Mrs. H.A. Ted Bailey, Jr., Miss Parma Basham, Mrs. Grainger Williams, and Mrs. John Samuel.

By December, we had acquired the names and addresses of hundreds of women obviously eager to help, but needing direction. We mimeographed a chart to send to them detailing things which needed to be done and, with the approval of each of the chairwomen heading each activity, we listed sixteen names *and* phone numbers. More and more women wanted to speak out; the results were exciting, building our momentum.

I can not emphasize too strongly the care we took with, and of, our membership list. Some of the women who gave us their names asked that nothing be mailed to their homes. Others asked that any mailings be sent in plain envelopes. Each card in our file had on it all of this information as well as indications of the talents of the women and the subcommittees to which they were assigned. We guarded this precious list painstakingly. As tensions worsened in the spring of 1959, a different woman took the file home each night to assure the secrecy of its location. We would protect our members from harassment if we possibly could.

At each of our monthly open meetings we had informative programs following our business sessions. Our first speaker was Mr. Maurice Mitchell, an attorney, who detailed for us the legal aspects of our school situation. The second was one of our own members, Carroll Holcomb, a graduate of Barnard College, wife of a contractor Norman Holcomb, who is a graduate of Columbia University. She spoke on the tax structure of the schools. The third was Mr. Wayne Upton, the president of the resigned school board. He related the history of the confused and tragic developments of 1957 and 1958. I needed to know the things these speakers said, but it was a rare meeting when I was free to hear the program. There were phone calls and there were urgent requests for private conferences, so all too often, following the business session, I spent the program time in Mrs. Terry's dining room where our executive committee regularly met, while the meeting proceeded in her parlors. I arranged for written reports of the talks and studied these in the evenings at home.

At every meeting there were strange faces so we had each woman sign in as she arrived in order to check her affiliation. At the December 2nd meeting just before the school board election, we were positive we had three spies with us. Barbara Ashmore laughed about it. "We are always bareheaded, but those women in the Mothers League do love those flowery hats." She did not know that I had a favorite broadbrimmed red hat with huge red flowers surrounding the crown. It became my custom to wear this when I spoke away from Little Rock. In fact, it

81

brought me my second favorite compliment. After the meeting in Fayetteville, at which I discussed the purpose of the WEC and the many laws affecting our schools, a woman in the audience said, "We talked about you again and again. Imagine: A woman like that in a hat like that."

We approached Christmas, and remembering the letters Mrs. Terry and I had from all over the nation and from other countries, we decided the WEC should send out a Christmas letter. We mimeographed this sheet by the thousands and supplied them to our members in any desired quantity. They in turn enclosed them with their personal Christmas greetings which fanned out over our United States and to many foreign shores. We later learned that many newspapers in other cities quoted from this brief Letter from Little Rock, and we were proud to reach new audiences with this message:

> We know it will be a long time before the state of Arkansas can live down the shame and disgrace with which it is now viewed by the entire world. We thought you might like to learn that there is one group here dedicated to the principle of good public education with liberty and justice for all. This group says to all the world there are many of us here who care enough to do something about this situation in which we find ourselves. I am proud and happy to be a member of the *Women's Emergency Committee to Open Our Schools.*
>
> Our aims are: to reopen our four public high schools; to retain our staffs of good teachers; and

to regain full accreditation by the North Central Association.

Meeting monthly in the gracious antebellum mansion of one of our founders, Mrs. David D. Terry, we have grown to include more than 850 members, plus uncounted persons who sympathize enough to contribute money even though they dare not become active members. We have an office and an efficient working organization. Knowing that ours is a task of education, we have sent out hundreds of letter — as individuals and as a committee — urging support of the public schools. We have mailed thousands of information leaflets urging the reopening of our schools, and we have presented radio, television, and newspaper material, as well as sponsoring meetings and furnishing speakers. We want our children, and indeed our nation, to be spared the cost of resolving any social conflict that can and should be worked out in the judicial atmosphere of our courts of law.

I wanted you to know that I am one of Little Rock's citizens who is deeply concerned about this problem.

It was the custom in my family to make much of Christmas, with elaborate decorations in our home, a large gathering of family and friends and a gourmet feast, but I gave only one day to this preparation in 1958,* and I remember only one thing about that Christmas day. Joe, who had been uncomplain-

---

* When I did retire in the fall of 1960, I discovered my collection of cook books, not one of which had been opened since September of 1958, riddled by bookworms. I had to burn most of them.

ing through these months of my neglect of the house, the garden and him, presented me with a broom to which he had attached a card bearing this plea: "Coya, come home."*

---

* Coya Knutson, Mrs. Harold Knutson, served as Representative from the Ninth District in Minnesota to the 84th and 85th sessions of Congress, 1954-1958. At the expiration of her term, as she lingered on in Washington, her husband's message to her, "Coya, come home," became a catch-phrase.

Five

If At First…

No day was long enough for all we wanted to do and no two days were alike. In addition to our executive board, we now had twenty-five committees working full time: art; attendance at school board meetings; club contacts; elections; feature articles; finance; flyers and ads; foreign visitors and exchange students; legislation; membership; messenger; night group; nominating; office staff; policy; projects; program; publicity; research and statistics; scrapbook; speakers bureau; state contacts; teacher contacts; telephone chain; TV and radio. After a conference with Mr. Maurice D. Bement, Regional Director of the National Citizens Council for Better Schools, who offered us generous supplies of TV and newspaper kits and outdoor displays, Anne Helvenston assembled a list of visual aids with detailed information about availability, content and cost. We mailed this data to many clubs, both within Little Rock and over Arkansas.

For a meeting of the publicity committee, I charted some suggestions:

> - Bombard the papers with letters, particularly the Democrat (Little Rock's evening paper which was read widely by our opposition). Sign with names less well known.
>
> - Try to get feature articles or letters in national magazines. These may be about our group or our problem.
>
> - Write letters to state weeklies stressing "This is not a local problem. It is yours, too."
>
> - Watch developments for ideas for flyers, for letters. We want to get out at least one flyer each week.
>
> - Watch for any opportunity to give the WEC favorable publicity. Stress the dignity, the policy and purpose of our group. Mention no controversial names. Clear all material with the executive committee.

We found letters published in the "Letters from the People" sections of the daily papers particularly effective. Some of them brought us hate mail. Our staff prepared many letters, which we passed on to members who were willing to sign them.

Membership Application for NAACP

Date _____

Name _____

Address _____

(if living in automobile, give Make, Model & License Number)

Race	Martial Status	Health
Ethiopian _____	Single _____	Gonorrhea _____
Mulatto _____	Married _____	Syphilis _____
Albino _____	Took-Ups _____	(answer "Yes"
African _____	not how many times)	
Nigger _____	*Children* Legitimate _____	
Passing White _____	Illegitimate _____	
Coon _____	(give accurate estimate)	
Panamanian _____		

Cigarettes	Whiskey	Automobile
Rabbit Tobacco _____	Bay Rum _____	Lincoln _____
Grape Vine _____	Moonshine _____	Cadillac _____
Marlboro _____	Hair Tonic _____	Oldsmobile ____
Butts _____	Canned Heat _____	Pontiac _____
Own Mixture _____		Buick _____

DO YOU BELONG TO ANY OF THE FOLLOWING ORGANIZATIONS?

Ku Klux Klan _____   Little Rock Nine _____

Communist Party _____   Alcoholics Anonymous _____

ARE YOU ASSOCIATED WITH ANY OF THE FOLLOWING?

Eleanor Roosevelt _____   Ed Sullivan _____   Richard Nixon ____

Ike Eisenhower _____   Felix Frankfurter _____   (any other SOB)

LIST ON THE BACK OF THE PAGE THE FLORIDA WHITE SCHOOL
YOU WOULD LIKE TO ATTEND. (Note: Georgia and Mississippi
schools are not integrateable.) DO NOT BE AFRAID TO ANSWER
THE ABOVE QUESTIONS. WE HAVE THE SUPREME COURT, THE
MODERN REPUBLIC, THE NORTHERN DEMOCRATS AND THE U.S.
ARMY ON OUR SIDE.

(Signature) _____

Hate mail sent to WEC

We asked them to copy our compositions in their own handwriting and to advise us when the letters were mailed so we could check the papers for the date of publication. When we discovered some of the letters were not being printed by the papers, we made contacts with the editors through friendly intermediaries to exert what influence we could.

In our sustained effort to tell the world that there were concerned citizens in Little Rock, I wrote a letter to the *Washington Post* in Washington, D.C., describing the work of our committee. We had a number of communications as a result of this, but the most interesting was a letter from a District of Columbia librarian, who sent us several books for our lending library and who for many months was an invaluable clipping service for us. He watched the Washington papers and the *New York Times* for articles bearing on the school situation and the desegregation problems, and he sent them to us neatly pasted on plain white paper, so many that they became a reference library in themselves. Not one of our members was more devoted to our cause than was William T. Purdum.

Another letter which I addressed to Washington had no answer at all. I first knew Bill Fulbright as a fraternity brother and close friend of my brother at the University of Arkansas. I knew his family background, his intellectual endowments, his educational opportunities. I was perplexed when he signed the Southern Manifesto, and shocked when, during the Little Rock crisis, he stayed away from Arkansas. In a statement quoted by the press, he inferred that other countries having minority problems excused our having them. In Atlanta, in December of 1958, he was quoted as saying that Chief Justice Warren and other justices of the Supreme Court were not qualified for their jobs. For a long time I worried about what I could say to him, how I could gain his support. Finally, following one quote on education in general, I wrote him a cautious letter which demanded no answer; so, although I expected one, I could not make an issue of the fact that I had none. My letter to him read:

Dear Bill:

We are in thorough accord with your statement as quoted in the attached clipping from the *Arkansas Democrat*. In this regard, we hope you will read and use the enclosed material.

Recently, a French representative of a South American newspaper came here to make a report because "Little Rock is the symbol of iniquity all over the world." Fortunately, he was here at the time of our first open night meeting which he attended. He told us of his amazement at finding the Women's Emergency Committee and he urged that we try to speak to all the world — that our voice could be a most effective force in bettering the foreign relations of our country.

We are proud that you, Bill, a fellow Arkansan, have the chance to be a leader in solving the imperative problem of World Peace. We want to help. We offer you our help, even though we have been deeply disappointed and dismayed that you have not tried to help us.

Most sincerely,
Vivion

February 19, 1959

Yet another letter addressed to Washington brought a disappointing answer. Our membership was growing gratifyingly, but there was a sizable group of women we were unable to touch. One of Little Rock's largest payrolls was the composite of the government installations, and there were numerous women so employed who would have liked to work with us, but feared accusations under the Hatch Act. "You know I'm with you 100%," said a friend slipping a bill into my hand, "but for heaven's sake don't use my name. You know why." This seemed a ridiculous fear when we were engaged only in a fight for public education, and I thought surely the Civil Service Commission would confirm my belief. This was our correspondence:

March 3, 1959

Civil Service Commission
Washington, D.C.

Gentlemen:

The enclosed leaflets will, in part, explain the policy and activities of our group. We were organized on September 16, 1958, with only fifty members. The immediate goal was to try to educate our voters to understand that they must vote "for integration" in the September 27 election or have our four high schools closed. Of course, we did not win, but we felt we had made a start and from that time our group has grown steadily until we now number more that 1,100, plus many friends whose sympathy and fear prompt them to send contributions anonymously.

We do not consider ourselves a political group. We do not feel that preserving a good public school system should be a political issue. We know that our program must be an educational one, to influence public opinion. This becomes a political program only in so far as we attempt to persuade citizens to vote in favor of our public school system, or as we talk with legislators trying to convince them that the destruction of our public school system is the destruction of our state. It is our policy to mention no names in our propaganda material or in our communications. We are a non-partisan group. We have taken no partisan action and we contemplate none.

Yet, when we ask a federal employee to address one of our meetings, we are told that he cannot do this. "There has been too much talk about the Hatch Act."

And when we ask federal employees to join our group, we are told they are afraid to. "Remember the Hatch Act."

We will be most grateful if you will give us a ruling as soon as possible making it clear that the Hatch Act does not apply to a group such as ours. Such a ruling would open the way to a wide expansion of our committee, both in numbers and in influence.

Sincerely yours,

Mrs. Joe R. Brewer

Chairman

UNITED STATES CIVIL SERVICE COMMISSION
Washington 25, D.C.

In Reply Please Refer
to GC: MLB: fw

Mrs. Joe R. Brewer
Chairman
Women's Emergency Committee to Open Our Schools
P.O. Box 122, Pulaski Heights Station
Little Rock, Arkansas

Dear Mrs. Brewer:

This is in reply to your letter of March 3rd enclosing literature relating to the policy and activities of the Women's Emergency Committee to Open Our Schools, of Little Rock, Arkansas. You request a ruling as to whether the Hatch Act would prohibit Federal employees from becoming members of the Committee inasmuch as they are reluctant to engage in the activities because of the Hatch Act.

The Hatch Act is directed at partisan activity in political campaigns. Political activity which is wholly nonpartisan and not identified with a National or state political party is permissible. This is stated in section 18 of the Hatch Act, which designates certain things as not being identified with a National or state political party, such as questions relating to constitutional amendments, referendums, approval of municipal ordinances, and other of similar character; see page 4 of the attached pamphlet. Also, your attention is called to section 21 of the Act which relates to officers and employees of educational institutions. This will be found on page 5 of the attached pamphlet.

Activity in connection with the question of re-opening the high schools in Little Rock would fall within the exceptions of section 18 of the Hatch Act, and would not be in contravention of the Hatch Act unless it should become identified with a National or state political party.

> Very truly yours,
> A.G. Clement, Chief
> Hatch Act and Litigation Section
> Office of the General Counsel.

I studied this long and intently and I could find in it no brief pointed ruling which we could use in flyers or ads, so I tried again:

March 28, 1959

Dear Mr. Clement:

Thank you for your letter of March 16. Your statements are reassuring to us as we were confident they would be. However, we are disappointed that, in the confused situation here, they are not sufficiently unequivocal to be used in publicity for our membership drives. Unfortunately your final clause "unless it should become identified with a National or state political party," which obviously eliminates us from any contravention of the Hatch Act, provokes arguments from citizens who think fuzzily or are looking for an excuse. We hoped for a firm statement which would allay all fears and convince even the most muddled thinker.

Would it be possible for you to give us a succinct and precise ruling, with permission to publish it? We would be most grateful.

> Very Sincerely,
> Mrs. Joe R. Brewer
> Chairman

In response, Mr. Clement wrote:

Dear Mrs. Brewer,

This is in acknowledgment of your letter of March 28 referring further to the application of the Hatch Act to Federal employees who become members of the Women's Emergency Commission to Open Our Schools of Little Rock, Arkansas. You request an unequivocal ruling on this question with permission to publish it.

We believe that the questions raised in your letter of March 3, 1959, were adequately answered in our letter of March 16, 1959, in which was enclosed for your information, a copy of the Commission's Pamphlet 20 entitled: Political Activity of Federal Officers and Employees. We are very glad to answer any questions you may have relating to the interpretation and application of the Hatch Act, but we do not do so for publicity purposes. Moreover, the Commission does not wish to become involved in local disputes of any kind. We believe that the letter sent to you March 16, 1959, is wholly unequivocal. The last clause of our letter of March 16 which you quote means exactly what it says, that is, that if a question or proposition such as municipal ordinances, referendum matters, constitutional amendments or other questions of a similar character, should become involved in partisan politics as a political party issue or as an issue raised in the campaign of a candidate in a partisan political election, then it might constitute prohibited political activity on the part of a Federal employee if he should become involved in it.

Very truly yours,
A.G. Clement, Chief

I had tried too hard and expected too much. We gave up our hope of soliciting memberships among government employees.

All of these months, and throughout the life of the WEC, scrapbooks were kept of our activities and of all related activities. They bulged with clippings which have been a valuable source of information in the years ensuing. A committee was appointed to maintain the WEC scrapbooks, and its chair, Bernice Sanders gave untold hours to keeping the scrapbooks current and in order.

In this busy spring of 1959, many inquiries prompted us to develop a form describing the WEC. We supplied this to help in membership and finance drives, and to mail with materials:

WOMEN'S EMERGENCY COMMITTEE
TO OPEN OUR SCHOOLS

P. O. Box 122, Pulaski Heights Station
Little Rock, Arkansas

The Women's Emergency Committee to Open Our Schools, organized last September in Little Rock, Arkansas, cites its policy and purpose as follows:

Dedicated to the principle of free public school education, and to law and order, we stand neither for integration nor for segregation, but for education. Our aims are to reopen Little Rock's four free public high schools; get students back in their classes; retain the staff of good teachers; and regain full accreditation.

The original group of 50 women now includes more than 1,400 members. Although the group has no

---

charter or by-laws, the organization is detailed and strong. Besides the four officers who are active daily, an Executive Committee of 12 meets each week to determine policy and projects, which are implemented through many sub-committees. All work is volunteer and is supported by contributions.

WHAT WE DO

Mail thousands of flyers to businessmen, legislators and parents.

Send letters to out-of-state friends, describing our purpose.

Write daily, commending stands in favor of public schools and answering statements opposing public schools.

Propose similar groups to other communities in the state; several have been organized.

Run weekly advertisements in the two Little Rock papers.

Relay messages to members via a telephone chain.

Maintain a lending library pertinent to our program; list related books available at the public library.

Arrange programs and announcements on TV and radio.

Seek voluntary financial support.

Staff an office with at least two typists daily.

Solicit ideas for flyers and other publicity, speakers, letter writers, book donors, volunteer typists and telephoners.

Call on legislators and study legislation.

Visit sessions of the House and the Senate, and School Board meetings, wearing badges.

We want the best possible education for all of our children and we are deeply concerned that they be spared the cost of resolving any social conflict which can and should be worked out in the judicial atmosphere of our courts of law. We welcome your comments, your suggestions and your advice, for we know you will realize that ours is not just a local problem, but one which is vital to the future welfare of our nation.

January of 1959 brought us another crisis as the state legislature convened and Governor Faubus, inaugurated for his third term, promised further school legislation to evade desegregation. The governor bragged about an average increase of $800 in classroom teachers' salaries during the last two years. He said that the average salary now was $3,216.00, "which is an all time high," and Arkansas no longer ranked last among the states. He failed to compare this figure with the national average, or divulge just where we did rank (47th). He made some frightening proposals:

In the field of controversy, state vs. federal power, I wish to recommend:

1. A constitutional amendment providing that by vote of the people, any school district may substitute a system of stu-

dent aid for the present system, pay to each student his pro-rata share of local funds, and the state will pay to each student his pro-rata share of state funds, so the student may attend any school he chooses.

2. Legislation to provide for adoption of the student aid system by any district, which is needed to cover the interim period between now and the adoption of the proposed amendment.

3. Provision for participation in a teacher retirement system by teachers who are now or may in the future be employed by private education institutions.

An editorial in the *Arkansas Gazette* on Saturday, January 17, sounded the only hopeful note: "... However, in proposing a state wide substitute for public schools, Mr. Faubus may have opened the eyes of some of those people who haven't at all minded seeing Little Rock going without public schools (and some who have even got a little vicarious pleasure out of the prospect) just so long as their own public schools were unaffected."

A delegation from the WEC led by Pat House called on the state senators and representatives from Pulaski County (in which county Little Rock is located) and brought to the executive committee a report on the attitudes of each one. We learned that these varied widely, from a future member of the Little Rock School Board who professed (at that time) to agree with us, to the one woman representative who, as a member of the board of the Private School Corporation, had failed to answer our plea that she support public education and who was now "non-committal," to the one outspoken ally of the governor who was "wild."

We organized a platoon of women and each day of the legislative session at least two of our members sat in the gallery of each chamber of the legislature, with small badges identifying their allegiance to the WEC. They were quiet, dignified, listening and watching. Whenever there was any important action on the floor, they hastened to report to our office by telephone.

Several bills slipped by with little debate, "spawned," as the *Washington Post* reported, "by anti-integration feeling." They were symptoms of our malaise:

> One required signatures of 25% of the qualified voters (instead of 15%) on petitions for recall elections;
>
> Another permitted teachers in private schools to share in teacher retirement benefits;
>
> Another appropriated $100,000 to aid school districts in court costs incurred in fighting integration;
>
> One authorized bus drivers to seat passengers at his discretion, and stipulated fines for passengers who refused to accept an assigned seat or leave the bus on request;
>
> One prohibited any member of the NAACP from holding jobs with a state, county, city or public school agency;

One required labeling of blood by race for transfusions;

The most frightening for us was Senate Joint Resolution No. 5, which proposed a constitutional amendment to appear on the ballot in the general election of November 1960. This amendment would provide for local option elections regarding the use of local and state money for education and could mean the complete destruction of the free public school system in the state, district by district. The fight to defeat this amendment was to absorb most of our time and energies throughout 1960.

I spent days writing up a synopsis of all of the Arkansas laws which threatened our school system. The final draft was edited by our attorney friend, Bob Shults, so we knew it was accurate and were confident about distributing this information over the state. In fact, we had need to refer to it frequently ourselves and to annotate it as the various courts were so frequently determining and re-determining the constitutionality of the laws.

Perhaps partly because of the constant and vigorous lobbying of our women, and our frantic and expensive calls and wires to every contact we could think of over the state, begging these contacts to send wires to representatives and senators in support of our schools, but more certainly because of the efforts of two courageous men, Senators Ellis Fagan and Sam Levine, we escaped two laws which would have spelled sure disaster for our schools.

On February 27, T.E. Tyler filed HB 546 to permit the governor to appoint three additional members to the Little Rock School Board, a sure means to control the Board. Mr. Tyler admitted this appeared to be dictatorial but he found sufficient excuse for it in the approval of the governor and of Ed McKinley, long a Faubus supporter and now president of the Little Rock School Board. A dozen of our women caught Mr. Tyler on the steps of the Capitol one bright day and, surrounding him, baffled him with staccato questions. A press photographer's delightful picture of this dramatic moment shows him a scared, bewildered man and includes the gleeful face of a "foreign" reporter avidly taking notes. The Pulaski County delegation in the House, excepting one, tried to stop this bill but was unsuccessful, obviously because it would affect only Little Rock. There was a jealousy of Little Rock throughout the state and the vote reflected this. It was not until Senator Ellis Fagan of Little Rock was able to have the bill tabled in the Senate that we breathed a grateful sigh of relief. Senator Fagan had not been exceptionally friendly to us, but this courageous action earned our loyalty and we worked hard for him in his next campaign.

A bill with a similar motive to stack the Little Rock Board, SB 421, was introduced by Senator Max Howell. This bill proposing the election of three additional members to the Little Rock School Board was stopped in the Senate by the filibuster of Senator Sam Levine of Pine Bluff, who later faced political defeat and untold harassment for this display of courage. When at last the legislature adjourned in the middle of March, Mr. Faubus assured the people that the fight for segregation was not over. He indicated that he had many more ideas for future legislation. We were thankful for a recess.

During these weeks of nerve-racking strain induced by the Faubus controlled law-making body, we were accelerating our drive for public education, and we gained some encouraging support and some helpful advice. On January 14, E. Grainger Williams, at the annual dinner meeting of the Little Rock Chamber of Commerce, of which he was president, jolted his audience with what now seem "quite innocuous" (his own words) remarks about the public schools:

> I cannot keep faith with myself, or with my concept of responsibility to you, as your newly elected president, without a frank statement to you, and a plea in the interest of public education. It is for this reason that I should like to say a few personal words in the interest of public schools.

> It is neither my purpose nor desire to discuss any of the political or sociological aspects of our school situation — nor do I have any solution to offer. But it is my feeling that the time has come for us to evaluate the cost of public education and the cost of the *lack* of public education.

> I would urge that no matter what our personal feelings might be... each of us encourage the re-establishment of all areas of communication, so that we may be able to discuss our principles... our feelings... our

differences... our problems without anger or hatred... without fear of reprisals... but with understanding, tolerance, intelligence and respect for each other.

To achieve this climate of communication would be one of the greatest contributions we could make, and to that end I am dedicated. As I said at the close of my official remarks: You, and only you, can determine the degree of success we shall enjoy.

With this stimulus, in early March the Chamber of Commerce polled its members and announced that 819 favored re-opening the schools with a plan of controlled minimum desegregation, 245 opposed reopening and 83 were silent. This was a vote of business men, and though it represented a comparatively small number and was anonymous, we rejoiced over it.

In January, Mrs. Jerome Levy called to ask if I would like to talk with Mr. Gus Falk, the regional executive secretary of the American Jewish Committee, who was in Little Rock. Indeed I would. I took Irene Samuel and Anne Helvenston with me to the synagogue to discuss public relations with Mr. Falk. This is my first memory of the major emphasis being placed on the "power structure," a term which has always annoyed me but for which I know no polite synonym. Mr. Falk drew a picture for us, a series of concentric circles, with the power structure in the center and the succeeding circles designated as

        a) organization
        b) community interest
        c) the fringe.

He felt that our name was bad, that it stressed the wrong idea. He advised that we change it, perhaps to "Women's Committee for Better Education," and that we begin to emphasize *danger*, not the hope of opening the schools but the disaster we faced by their destruction. I gained many new thoughts from this conference, but I was confident that the name of the WEC had become so well known that we would only hurt ourselves by changing it. Some of our members hated this cumbersome name but the executive committee agreed that WEC should be here for the duration.

Help came also from the regional office of the Anti Defamation League in New Orleans. Irving Schulman, director of that office, contacted us, met several times with our executive committee and kept in touch with us throughout the life of the WEC. He offered not only information and advice but supplied us with many materials.

Two members of the Friends Service Committee, from the Texas Division, came to Little Rock, made a study and gave us the benefit of their assessment of the situation. They were particularly concerned about the Negro young people from the closed Horace Mann High School. Too few of them had found enrollment in another school. And yet, they told us, Mrs. Daisy Bates, state representative of the NAACP, insisted they wanted no substitute for the public schools since this would circumvent their ideal of integrated schools. These two Friends shocked us with their apprehension that Mr. Jess Matthews, principal of Central High School, really

didn't care where his pupils were. I could not believe this until 1966 when he vocally supported the
race of T.E. Tyler for Lt. Governor. If he had any
memory of Mr. Tyler's attempt to pack the Little Rock
School Board and so assure the continued closure
of the Little Rock high schools, how could he have
believed Mr. Tyler would be suitable for the position
of Lt.-Governor? (Mr. Tyler did not win.)

The Friends Service Committee sent into Little
Rock an attractive and helpful person, Thelma Babbitt. She began work immediately, seeing all the
people she could, of both races, trying to improve
communication between the white and Negro communities. She asked me to meet her for tea and I
went gladly, but came away disturbed that I had
not been able to convince her that the WEC must,
for *this* time, remain a group of white women. She
developed a group of both white and Negro concerned persons who met in open sessions at
Aldersgate Camp, the Methodist retreat west of Little
Rock. These meetings were not publicized and they
were a wonderful outlet for me. Here I could think
and hear and talk racial relations, and I learned
much, and made many new friends. When Mrs.
Babbitt, following a siege of infectious hepatitis, had
to leave Little Rock, I spent months trying to find a
man willing to serve as the chairman of a "Community Unity" group, to assure the continuance of the
movement. It was the same old story, even among
those now dedicated to our program. Business men,
professional men, representatives of labor, retired
and independent men — each had some excuse.

Desperate friends urged that I assume the chairmanship myself but I knew this was not the answer. After months, many months of earnest hope, this group which Mrs. Babbitt had fostered, disintegrated. It was with wry amusement that I read in 1966, in our local papers, that a series of meetings of very similar pattern was the "first one" ever developed in Little Rock.

Harry Ashmore sent us word that the Southern Regional Council would pay the expenses of the field secretary of the Virginia Committee for Public Schools, if we'd like him to visit us for a day's conference. We were only too glad for any assistance. We welcomed Mr. William M. Lightsey late in February, and when we bade him goodbye we felt the SRC's money had been well spent. Mr. Lightsey was on leave from the U.S. Department of Agriculture where he was chief of the Acreage Reserve Branch, Soil Bank Division, Community Stabilization Service. He was serving a three year term as Director of the Northern District of the Virginia Congress of Parents and Teachers. He met with our officers and the executive committee at Mrs. Terry's home. At noon, about ten of the attorneys and business men who had been sympathetic were invited to join us for a luncheon-discussion meeting. These included the president of the Chamber of Commerce, three members of the Little Rock School Board, and two leaders of the Little Rock Bar Association.

Mr. Lightsey came armed with leaflets and pamphlets and much concrete advice stemming from the history of the development of the Virginia Committee and its successes.* Among terse comments he made, I remember especially: "Alienate no one. Call no one a segregationist or he will immediately call you an integrationist. Use the term extremist. Do not use the name of anyone known to be too liberal." He thought we should admit men to our membership but our executive board disagreed with him about this. (Unbeknownst to us, we did have a few men's names in our membership files.) Another suggestion was that we publish an ad to be signed by one hundred men of prominence. This appealed strongly. We worked hard on the wording of such a statement and I talked with the men friendly to us about it but nothing ever came of it. The men of Little Rock were not yet roused to the point of speaking out. Mr. Lightsey thought we might issue a card to members containing a statement for their signature, as a psychological emphasis on their concern. We considered this idea at length but decided against it in the continued atmosphere of harassment and fear in our city. The situation in Virginia and in Little Rock seemed so alike and yet so unlike that it was difficult to suit their tactics to our needs, but our executive committee eagerly considered every suggestion. Deeply as we appreciated all offers of help and were encouraged by them, we tried to make every decision objectively, and all of

---

* We were never able to equal the 18,000 membership of the Virginia Committee, but then, Governor Faubus was not Governor Almand; we had no paid staff; the defeat of amendment 52 in 1960 seemed to quiet any statewide concern for the local schools in Arkansas.

our actions were the result of our own determination.

One of our most heartening visitors was the Reverend Will D. Campbell, the Associate Executive of the Department of Racial and Cultural Relations of the National Council of the Churches of Christ in Nashville, Tennessee. When I returned to the office from a tiring and futile trip to a business office one afternoon, I found him talking to an unusually happy Irene. There was all too little to laugh at in those days; his biting humor cheered both of us and helped us attack our problems with renewed faith. All who shared his subsequent letters enjoyed their amusing and amused comments on humanity, such as this letter of April 8, 1959:

Dear Mrs. Brewer:

It was nice visiting with you and members of the Women's Emergency Committee to Open Our Schools last week. You should know that the work of this Committee is encouraging to people throughout the country, many of whom reside in the South, and you are to be commended for this kind of sacrificial service.

I regret that the group of which I am a member has not seen fit to offer you more support. I hope that the statement you were preparing when I was with you has met with some success.

I am enclosing a statement which was prepared and signed by officials of social action departments of the various Protestant nation and you are free to use it in any way you see fit. Though it does not speak to your immediate situation and needs, it is directed at some of the opposition which you encounter.

Please feel free to call on me as an individual or this office as the Southern wing of one department of the National Council of Churches. Unfortunately, that is all I can commit but I assure you that my services will be forthcoming any time a request is made.

Personal regards to you, Mrs. Cotton, Mrs. Samuel, Mrs. Terry and others of the Little Rock Sisterhood. I have started a one-man campaign in gaining for you the title of St. Vivion of Little Rock. I expect this candidization to be official eventually, though I am bestowed upon you by a renegade Southern Baptist. Since, to my knowledge, no Southern Baptist has ever elevated a person to sainthood before, you will at least be unique.

Cordially Yours,

Will D. Campbell

Associate Executive

At the time of this visit, we were working on a statement supporting public education which we hoped to publish when we had secured sufficient signatures of local ministers. We worded it with caution, so we thought:

It is our belief that our public school system must be preserved, and our prayer that our four closed high schools shall be open in September. The harmful impact of school closing on the welfare of our children, on the economic health of our community and on the future growth of our city and state is inestimable, and an inadequate school system may well promote discouragement, frustration and delinquency.

As citizens and as religious leaders, we urge our churches in obedience to God and under His blessing to encourage within their congregations a free and intelligent discussion of the issues we confront, and we appeal to our community and state leaders to give their most creative thought to maintaining a sound public school plan with respect for law and order.

We assembled lists of volunteers from the various denominations who would call on the many ministers, and I went to see the Reverend Colbert S. Cartwright, pastor of the Pulaski Heights Christian Church, who was president of the Arkansas Council on Human Relations and a member of the board of the Southern Regional Council. From the beginning he had been staunchly vocal and his congregation had supported him. He was not encouraging. "I'll sign it, of course," he said, "but you might as well know we have tried for months — more than a year — to get a statement from the Ministerial Alliance, but there's always somebody to object to some word of some phrase." It was not long until his suspicions were confirmed. I remember so well my visit with the minister of a prominent Baptist Church. He told me repeatedly that his views were liberal and that he approved our objective, but he would not sign the statement unless we eliminated the phrase, "We urge our churches in obedience to God and under his blessing." If we changed even one word, it obviously meant repeated visits to many ministers who had already signed, but for a couple of months we persevered, laboring with semantics, in spite of replies such as: "If you get so many signatures, then I will sign"; and out and out refusals. We knew of the persecution of the ministers who had been brave enough to speak for the brotherhood of man. Several had been transferred out of the state; most of those who were allowed to stay were warned by influential members of their congregations that they must be silent on this subject "or else." But we maintained the hope that this incredible facet of so-called Christianity must disappear. This was one of our disheartening failures. There were approximately four-hundred ministers in Little Rock at this time, but when we finally abandoned our desire to publish this statement, we had only twenty-five signatures: seven Baptist (two more promised); eight Presbyterian; three Methodist; two Episcopalian; three Christian. Two Rabbis signified a desire to sign although one of them very properly asked that we add "and synagogues" following "we urge our churches . . ."

The other failure of 1959 which was to make 1960 such a difficult year was our attempt to form a state-wide Arkansas Committee for Public Schools. Local groups, even though small, were functioning. A friend in Conway, realizing that she could involve more women in a state group than in a local unit, invited us to her home; we had an encouraging day with some 15 concerned women. Irene Samuel, Janet Johnston and I explained our policy and our program and we found friendship and enthusiasm. Another time, the three of us went to Pine Bluff to meet with an interested group. That was the day the Chamber of Commerce had a half page ad reading:

Therefore we recommend, based solely on the reason that we desire to seek a solution acceptable to a large majority of the people of Little Rock:

1. The continuation and community support of high schools in Little Rock operating with private funds.

2. The reopening of the Little Rock Public High Schools by using a pupil assignment system acceptable to the school board and the federal courts.

3. The School Board assuring all teachers that their contracts will be promptly renewed in order that we do not lose our valuable and loyal staff.

4. Accepting the responsibility to seek new laws in Congress that would return the operation of public schools to each individual school district, regardless of the outcome of our present school crisis.

Clauses 1 and 4 were depressing but we told

ourselves that these statements were necessary in order to bring the membership of the Chamber of Commerce forward with its leadership. I realized this because for months I had felt the same caution in our own organization. One of the joys of my dedication to our committee was seeing changing attitudes among the women who began first to work only for open schools and who before too many months professed not only an acceptance but often a preference for desegregation of the schools.

These local units, and I must not forget Fayetteville, the seat of the University of Arkansas, where we had our greatest strength outside of Little Rock, were not the answer to our total plan. We were convinced that Little Rock's dilemma was not an isolated one. If the schools remained closed in the capital city, who could guess how quickly this destruction of education would move over the state? We sent bulletin after bulletin to every leader in every county and in every city and in every town. We sent personal letters to anyone whose name was submitted to us as a possible cohort. We developed a three page explanation of the need for a state-wide committee. I literally spent months trying to obtain the approval of sufficient men of the power structure to develop an executive board which might influence timid citizens in the seventy-five counties of our state. Some of the contacts had to be by letter, but many were personal, and while there were occasional lifts of my spirit, most of the answers were the perennial negative. "I can be of more influence if I am aligned with no group."

"I can not afford to have my name known with any group."

"I do not like the wording of paragraph... , but I will study this and send you my suggestions."

(I can not recall a single altered statement which was ever returned to the office.) Some were frank enough to admit their fear of reprisals.

Some excuses were ludicrous. "I am on the Water Commission."

Volunteers kept accurate accounts of addressees and their responses. I checked them frequently, ever hopeful, but finally the executive committee saw that this potential and much needed organization did not have enough state-wide support to get it off the ground. The men were still underground or somewhere else.

Perhaps we antagonized, even frightened the power structure, for we stubbornly refused to be silent. A friendly attorney, Tom Downie, with the enthusiastic support and generous cooperation of Ed Lester and Bob Shults, agreed to file an *amicus curiae* — friend of the court — brief for us in the Gertie Garrett case, also known as the Coffelt case, a test of the school closing law, Act No. 4 of the special session of 1958. Our counsel obtained permission to file this brief, estimating its cost to us at about $350.00. It was an excellent brief of which we were proud, but the case went against us. On April 28, the Arkansas Supreme Court by a four to three vote upheld Act 4 of 1958; it was not until June 18th that a three Judge Federal Court overruled the Arkansas Supreme Court and held both Acts 4 and 5 unconstitutional.

When Tom submitted his bill for the preparation of the brief, the costs of printing and incidentals, we found we owed nearly $1,000. Rather to my surprise, the executive committee raised no question about this, despite the great disparity between the final bill and our original estimate, and we made no point of it with Tom Downie. I do not know if this speaks for our rash optimism, our gratitude for any male assistance, or our affluence. In Tom's defense, I must add that he later gave us much free aid when we faced possible persecution by some of the City Directors.

Under a Bruce Bennett (state Attorney General) ordinance which had been aimed at the NAACP, one of the city directors, Hardy Winburn — so we were told — insisted on obtaining a list of our membership. Through our sanguine friend, Mrs. Dixon, City Attorney Joseph Kemp asked for an interview. With Mrs. Dixon, I went to his office. The curtains were drawn; the lights were dim. He sat behind a handsome mahogany desk. The entire plush atmosphere was such a shocking contrast to the make-shift, harried, crowded decor of the WEC office that I suddenly felt as though I must be dreaming. "All I ask," Mr. Kemp assured me, "is a list of your membership."

"But this is exactly what I refuse to give to you,"

I responded. "Don't you see that the only reason it is wanted is for harassment, for reprisals? I will not make this possible — not for one single woman if I can help it."

I was terribly upset and Mrs. Dixon looked at me in surprise. "I'd never thought of that," she admitted. "Of course I see what you mean." The city attorney saw, also — who wouldn't have? — and he ultimately agreed to submit a letter from me swearing that we had no membership list, only a mailing list.

While I was trying to make up my mind how to word this letter, which I never did write, we had a more direct demand for the names of our members. Another of the city directors had decided to make a try for himself. I have some doubts that the Board of Directors sponsored or even sanctioned this, but they did not express any disapproval of it. On March 29, a Friday night, two Little Rock plain clothes officers delivered a letter in person to our secretary, Mrs. Woodbridge Morris:

March 27, 1959

Mrs. Woodbridge E. Morris, Secretary,
Women's Emergency Committee to Open Our Schools

Dear Mrs. Morris:

Pursuant to the provisions of Ordinance No. 10,638 of the City of Little Rock, Arkansas, you, as Secretary of the Women's Emergency Committee to Open Our Schools, are hereby requested to furnish the City Clerk of Little Rock with the following information regarding the said WEC to OOS:

A. The official name of the organization;

B. The office, place of business, headquarters or usual meeting place of such organization.

C. The officers, agents, servants, employees or representatives of such organization, and the salaries paid to them.

D. The purpose or purposes of such organization.

E. A financial statement of such organization, including dues, fees, assessments and/or contributions paid, by whom paid, and the date thereof, together with the statement reflecting the disposition of such sums, to whom and when paid, together with the total net income of such organization.

F. An affidavit by the president or other officiating officer of the organization stating whether the organization is subordinate to a parent organization, and if so, the name of the parent organization.

A list containing this information must be furnished the City Clerk of Little Rock, Arkansas, c/o City Hall, Markham and Broadway Streets, Little Rock, Arkansas, within fifteen (15) days from the date that this request is received by you.

Very sincerely,
Letcher L. Langford
Member of the Board of Directors
of the City of Little Rock, Arkansas

Mrs. Morris' husband, a busy physician, and her two teen-age sons were away. The sight of the detectives frightened her dreadfully. Had some horrible accident occurred? The reality of the letter was a minor worry in comparison, but it demanded some careful thought. After all, we had consistently spoken of our increasing membership and of asking $1.00 from each member. My letter to the Washington Post had mentioned our membership dues of $1.00. We needed legal advice and I talked with Tom Downie and his partner, Edwin Dunaway, at some length. As a result, the WEC, over the signature of the secretary, submitted both to the city clerk and to Mr. Letcher L. Langford the following:

SENT REGISTERED RETURN RECEIPT REQUESTED

April 1, 1959

City Clerk
c/o City Hall
Markham and Broadway Streets
Little Rock, Arkansas

Dear Sir:

Complying with the letter from Mr. Letcher L. Langford, member of the Board of Directors of the City of Little Rock, Arkansas, dated March 27, the WEC to OOS is filing with you the requested information hereto attached.

Yours truly,
Mrs. Woodbridge E. Morris
Secretary

dm/b
enclosures

SENT REGISTERED RETURN RECEIPT REQUESTED

April 1, 1959

Mr. Letcher L. Langford
Member of the Board of Directors
of the City of Little Rock, Arkansas

Dear Mr. Langford:

Complying with your letter of March 28, the WEC to OOC is today filing with the City Clerk of Little Rock, Arkansas, c/o City Hall, Markham and Broadway Streets, Little Rock, Arkansas, the requested information, a copy of which is enclosed.

Yours truly
Mrs. Woodbridge E. Morris
Secretary

dm/b
enclosures

I, the undersigned, Mrs. Joe R. Brewer, chairman of the WEC to OSS, do hereby state and swear that the said committee is subordinate to no parent organization.

/s/   Mrs. Joe R. Brewer
Vivion L. Brewer
chairman

Signed and sworn to before me this 12th day of February, 1959

/s/   Roger C. Richards
Notary Public

WOMEN'S EMERGENCY COMMITTEE
TO OPEN OUR SCHOOLS
P.O. BOX 122, PULASKI HEIGHTS STATION
LITTLE ROCK, ARKANSAS

Total Expenditures: 9-19-58 to 3-31-59

Printing, stationery, mailing permit, stamps, post cards, etc.	$ 1558.36
Office and hall expense, telephones, rent, etc.	132.72
Newspaper and TV advertising	2602.49
Public Relations Service	275.00
Attorney fee (Retainer for Brief, Ark. Supreme Court)	750.00
Film rentals	8.30
Bank charges	5.42
	$ 4910.85

Total Income: 9-19-58 to 3-31-59 $ 8775.56

No detailed records are maintained which reflect sources of income. All income is derived from voluntary contributions.

as submitted:

Total expenditures: 9-19-58 to 3-31-59

Stationary, printing, mailing, telephones, etc.	$ 1558.36
Newspaper and TV ads, public relations services	2602.49
Legal services	750.00
	$ 4910.85

Total Income: 9-19-58 to 3-31-59 $ 8770.56

---

with statement; "No detailed records... etc."

LETTER FROM **LITTLE ROCK**

We know it will be a long time before Little Rock and the state of Arkansas can live down the shame and disgrace which have brought them publicity throughout the entire world. But perhaps you have not heard that there is one group here dedicated to the principle of good public education with liberty and justice for all. I am very proud to be a member of the WOMEN'S EMERGENCY COMMITTEE TO OPEN OUR SCHOOLS, an organization that is eager to have the world know we are working very hard to overcome the critical situation in which we find ourselves.

Our aims are: to reopen our four public high schools; to retain our staffs of good teachers; and to regain full accreditation by the North Central Association. We stand neither for integration nor for segregation, but for education and for law and order.

Organized last September, with only 50 women at the first meeting, we have grown to include more that 1000 members plus uncounted persons who sympathize enough to contribute money even though they dare not become members. We have an office and an efficient staff. Our executive committee meets once a week to hear reports of the many special committees. The entire committee, including a day group, and a night group for business and professional women, meets once a month. Interest has been expressed outside Little Rock and similar groups have been formed in many other cities and communities throughout the state.

Knowing that ours is a task of education, we have sent out hundreds of letters, as individuals and as a committee, urging support of the public schools. We have mailed thousands of information leaflets urging the reopening of our schools, and we have presented radio, television and newspaper material. We have a Speakers Bureau, and a lending library. We want the best possible education for all of our children and we are deeply concerned that they be spared the cost of resolving any social conflict which can and should be worked out in the judicial atmosphere of our courts of law.

We welcome your comments, your suggestions and your advice, for we know you will realize that ours is not just a local problem, but one which is vital to the future welfare of our nation.

We hoped this would be the end of it but this failed to satisfy Mr. Langford and on April 10, he renewed his request of Mrs. Morris:

April 10, 1959

Dear Mrs. Morris

The information furnished by you, as Secretary of the WEC to OOS to the City Clerk of LR, Ark, as requested of you by a letter dated March 27, 1959, pursuant to the provisions of Ordinance No. 10,638 failed to comply with Section E of said ordinance, in that you did not include in the financial statement the names of persons making contributions or paying dues or assessments, the dates thereof, nor the names of persons receiving disbursements from your organization, the dates thereof and a statement of the net income of your organization.

You are hereby requested to furnish all of the information required by Section E of said Ordinance No. 10,638 to the City Clerk of LR, Ark, c/o City Hall, Markham & Broadway Sts, Lr, Ark, within fifteen (15) days from the date this request is received by you.

Very sincerely,
Letcher L. Langford
Member of the Board of Directors
of the City of LR, Ark

This letter was delivered to her in person by detectives on Monday night, April 13. She recognized the source this time but she was none the less disturbed. I tried to make light of Mr. Langford's autocratic attempts at harassment, but I was not, secretly, as confident as I tried to sound. I went again to see Tom Downie and Ed Dunaway, and Ed had a brilliant suggestion which pleased *him* very much. "It is about time some of you go to jail," he advised, "you and Dottie, and how about someone as respectable as Miss Hildegard Smith?" (She had taught music in Little Rock for years, was on the National Board of the Musical Coterie.) When I reported this, Dottie did not think it funny at all. She was nervous and upset by these tactics of Mr. Langford, and although in my heart I thought it not an outrageous idea for some of us to be temporary martyrs, indeed one worth trying, my husband was not a bit amused at the thought of my going to jail. So Ed's idea never did materialize; yet some of us were willing to try almost anything to jolt public opinion. One young woman told me one day, "I've thought about hiring some seg to shoot me. Maybe an attempted murder would bring Faubus to his senses."

We wrote another and more lengthy letter to Mr. Langford, and since we were giving all of this to the press, we tried to be light and humorous:

April 23, 1959

Dear Sir:

We have received your letter of April 10, 1959, requesting the WEC to OOS to file additional information under Section "E" of City Ordinance No. 10638.

We have been advised by our legal counsel that the report heretofore submitted to the City Clerk contains all the information necessary for a determination that ours is not an organization operated for profit, and, therefore, is not subject to obtaining an occupational license.

In the report which we previously filed, we stated that our income is from voluntary contributions, and that detailed records of members or contributors are not kept. We collect no dues and make no assessments. The only profit with which we are concerned is the welfare of our children, our community and our state.

In your most recent letter, you state that we did not give a statement of our net income. In our original report we showed a total income of $8,777.56 and total expenditures of $4,910.85. We had assumed that the difference in these two

---

---

figures would show our net income. For your convenience, we now make that subtraction:

$$\begin{array}{r} \$8,777.56 \\ \underline{4,866.85} \\ \$3,866.71 \end{array}$$

This balance, and any other money received by us, will be used in non-profit activities to achieve the objectives of our organization as stated in our earlier report.

We wish to say that we are impressed with your zeal in seeing that proper financial support for needed municipal services is obtained from all who should be paying an additional tax. In this connection, we might point out that the U.S. mails are available for the delivery of communications to us. We suggest that future communications be sent by this means, rather than by taking the time of our undermanned police force to deliver your letters, as has been done on the past two occasions.

We assure you of our continued desire to co-operate with the City in the conduct of its affairs. If the City Collector has any questions about our non-profit status, we will be happy to have him go over our records of income and expenditures.

/s/   Yours truly
                              Dorothy Wells Morris
                          Mrs. Woodbridge E. Morris
                                          Secretary

But Mr. Langford was adamant. A third letter from him was dated April 26. This was delivered by a member of the Little Rock police department, in mufti. Mr. Langford was quoted as saying that using policemen to deliver such letters was "a long-established custom of the city." He added that officers were on the lookout for law violators while they were on these trips. This third letter follows:

April 26, 1959

Dear Mrs. Morris:

Several organizations have been asked to comply with Ordinance No. 10638 and all complied promptly but the NAACP. The NAACP did not want the public to know who their members and contributors were. The City of Little Rock had Daisy Bates, the President, arrested and she was fined in the Little Rock Municipal Court. The fine was upheld in the Circuit Court and the Arkansas Supreme Court.

The Women's Emergency Committee to Open Our Schools publicly claims a membership of 1,200. Is the Women's Emergency Committee to Open Our Schools also afraid to comply with our law of the land?

You state that your organization collected $8,770.56 in less than six and one-half months, but that in effect you do not know who contributed it. Do you think the Little Rock Officials, the Court or the Public will believe that? All we are asking you to do is to comply with Ordinance No. 10638, not in just some points, but in all points. The Ordinance provides a fine of not less than $50.00 nor more than $250.00 for failing to comply, with each day being a separate offense. You are again requested to furnish a list of your contributors in accordance with the Ordinance.

Very sincerely,
/s/ Letcher L. Langford
Member of the Board of Directors
of the City of Little Rock, Arkansas

This letter, remarking on our statement that we had collected $8,770.56 in less than six and a half months, frightened our donors. I spent hours reassuring our women that no records would be available to anyone, that no contributor need have a moment of worry because of his support of the WEC, that all businessmen must know that we would never divulge the name of anyone who had ever given us a penny, unless he authorized us to do so. As a matter of fact, our books were seldom more explicit than a bank statement.

Our final letter to Mr. Langford was sent by special delivery, and with the sarcasm in its fourth paragraph thoroughly relished by our friends, this was the end of our communication:

> May 4, 1959
>
> Dear Mr. L:
>
> This will acknowledge your letter of 4/25/59, concerning the applicability of LR City Ord No. 10638 to the WEC, and we are somewhat bewildered at its belligerent and threatening tone. It has been our earnest belief that we were complying with both the spirit and the letter of that ordinance, and these views have been shared by our legal counsel. The last thing that our women wish to do is to be at cross purposes with civic-minded officials like yourself, since we share with you the common objective of the betterment of our community.
>
> We regret very much that we are unable to supply you with an accurate list either of our members or our contributors. If anonymous persons sig-

nify a vital interest in our work, we count them as members. For various reasons, many names given to us have been placed on different mailing lists. Obviously any list we would supply to you could not possibly be a complete list. As to contributors, we refer you to our two previous letters on this subject in which you were advised that no detailed records of contributors are kept on sources of income, and that no dues or assessments are made or collected.

In your latest communication, in referring to our failure to keep detailed records of our contributions, you asked, "Do you think the LR Officials, the Court or the Public will believe that?" We assure you we would not have made the statement had it not been true, and our answer to your question is yes, we fully expect our public officials and the public to believe this. After all, it is from the public that our contributions have come — in many cases anonymously — and in all cases without record. In our last letter to you on April 10, we invited you to verify the truth of this yourself. To date, the City Collector has not made inquiry of us concerning our financial records, but the offer remains in effect, and we will be glad at any time to go over our records with him.

In view of the extreme personal concern which you expressed in your last letter as to the names of our contributors, the committee feels that it should make every effort to help you obtain these names of which we have no record. We are, therefore, calling publicly upon all persons who have contributed in any way to this committee, to convey their names and the amount of their contributions directly to you, either by telephone or by mail, if they desire to do so. In this way you will not have to depend on our busy volunteer staff to relay this information to you.

This letter was prepared under the direction of the Ex. Com. of this group whose names we furnished you previously, and is being sent to you at their request.

Yours very truly,
Mrs. W.E.M.
Sec.

There was no doubt that we did not have the City Directors with us. Also there was no doubt we must erase two words from our vocabulary; member and membership. From then on we had *only* a mailing list. But it was ironic that the April issue of *Progressive* carried a letter from me quoting our Christmas letter which ended, "We are supported entirely by contributions and $1.00 membership fees."

Despite all of these interruptions of our work, we explored all possibilities of a solution of our educational crises. We listened to the proposals of two very different men, and we studied them and discussed them fully. Jimmy Karam, the acknowledged friend of Governor Faubus, phoned to ask if he might meet with our executive committee. Mrs. Terry immediately said, "Tell him to come."

I was more timid or more repelled than she by the thought of being in the same room with this man who figured so prominently in the 1957 riot. "I wouldn't want him in *my* house," I objected.

"Honey," Adolphine laughed, "Let's use anybody we can; anybody." So he came and sat with our board in Mrs. Terry's dining room and urged us to consider his program. I've always wished we'd been as bright as some of our adversaries and had arranged for a tape of Mr. Karam's impassioned presentation. My notes show his suggestions included:

1. Segregation of students by sex.

2. Health tests for all and suspension of those with communicable diseases.

3. Achievement tests for all, with white's and Negro's identical, and placement in schools solely on basis of tests.

4. Highest moral codes for all students, with unwed mothers banished from classroom and no immoral conduct permitted.

I appointed a committee to study his proposals in depth, but from the beginning I knew I'd be phoning him to say nay. To my surprise, he offered no rebuttal at all, just meekly said, "Well, all right." I've always wondered why he came. None of us could offer a very plausible explanation, unless it was that he and the governor hoped that the WEC would accept his suggestions and disband.

The Very Reverend Charles A. Higgins, Dean of Trinity Episcopal Cathedral, gave an interview to the *Gazette* early in January, indicating he had firm ideas for a way to reopen the schools. I asked if a few of our women might visit with him about this and he readily agreed. His suggestions involved such drastic changes in our public education that we did not feel they would be acceptable to the WEC or to the general public, but once more we gave a new plan thorough consideration. Velma Powell's notes presented to our executive committee are indicative of our reactions:

Notes of conference with Dean Higgins

Mrs. Banner, Mrs. Brewer Mrs. Morris, Mrs. Powell

Proposed Plan in General

Based on British Colonial system of schools.

Separate by sexes. Specifically grades 1 through 8.

Possibly have no coeducational college preparatory school. Entrance to be determined by record in first eight years of school. Possible entrance examination. Have "trade school" for boys and one for girls.

Delete from curriculum all "frills" Such as extracurricular activities. Something on the order of the "Latin Grammar Schools."

Points of personal concern (Mrs. Powell)

Premise that entire system of public education must be changed.

Statement that local educators had little to do with forming policies and procedures but did what the National Education Association told them to do. (The Dean used "American Education Association.")

Said we could not deny that the public schools had done a good job of teaching "relations." Said at the moment he was counseling with two girls who wanted to marry Jews. The girls could see nothing wrong with this.

In-service training would have to start immediately for teachers to give them the "new" philosophy of education.

Central High School had no discipline. He had walked through the halls and the noise and confusion was awful.

From people he had talked to he felt Raney High was offering as good a program as Central had offered.

My deep concern lies in the feeling I came away with that Dean Higgins thinks our American System of Public Education is <u>all</u> wrong and the fact that he feels teaching "relations" is also wrong. I personally believe so strongly in the rightness of the American System of Education, and also in the teaching of relations and understanding of all groups, that I may not be completely objective.

We were shocked by Dean Higgins' subsequent statements in the newspaper, and our executive committee prepared a mild disapproval of his attitude:

> Thank you very much for talking to the representatives of our Women's Emergency Committee to Open Our Schools. We assure you of our total interest in any workable solution of our present impasse which will preserve our free public education system. We believe this to be your interest also.

We were, therefore, disturbed by a statement in yesterday's *Gazette* purported to contain a quote from you as follows: "He said it was likely that the public junior high schools would soon be closed if we continue our policy of retreating before the onslaught of NAACP legal actions." In view of the present tensions in our city, we are sure you will agree with our executive committee that this statement was misleading and therefore unfortunate. I am sure you regret the implication more than we do.

This asked no answer and elicited none.

Even as we sought advice from any quarter, we tried to help anywhere we could. Atlanta was facing the possible disruption of the city's educational system, and concerned citizens decided to organize a committee similar to ours which they would call HOPE (Help Our Public Education). They asked if we would send a speaker to their first open meeting. Mrs. Terry could not go, for family reasons. I felt utterly inadequate. One of the members of the steering committee, Mrs. Gordon N. Wilson — Billie Wilson — agreed to go. The concerned mother of a displaced high school student, she won her audience. Staying on for a day, she met with the officers, and I talked with the leaders of HOPE by phone to clear some questions on organization and legal aspects which Billie felt unable to answer. For months, Billie corresponded with these women and through Billie, the WEC kept contact with HOPE, sharing many perilous experiences.

Much later, we sent materials and wires and letters of encouragement to the committee of women struggling in New Orleans — S.O.S. — (Save Our Schools). At the time of the ordeal at the University of Mississippi, I made a trip to deliver materials from our committee to the Reverend Duncan Gray, Jr. so that he might pass them on to the concerned women in Jackson, who were compelled to work underground in those frightening days. It is unbelievable that after we parked our car on the campus in Oxford, Mississippi to meet a young chaplain on the grounds, he warned us that our license would have been spotted and identified, and he urged us not to tarry.

We were constantly thinking of ways to convince the world that not everyone in Little Rock had horns. One night a long distance call came over our home phone from Washington, D.C. The caller was one of the staff of the USIS who chanced to know relatives of mine in Washington and through them had heard of our committee. "There is a gentleman here from Nigeria," he told me. "He wants very much to see Little Rock. Would you undertake setting up a two or three day program for him?"

My mind somersaulted as I thought of entertaining a member of the black race in these tense times and I wondered how my neighbors on the party line would react to this. I only hoped they had not triggered to the meaning of USIS nor to the location of Nigeria. "This is an opportunity we must not miss."

I told myself. "Of course, send him along," I told Lamar King. To my delight, the executive committee welcomed this new adventure, and one of the women, Parma Basham, immediately offered to give a dinner party for Mr. Saidu Garba. He came, wearing his native robe and turban, and there was no problem about his staying at a Little Rock hotel or eating in its restaurant. I think Mr. Garba enjoyed his visit and left with an altered opinion of our city and its people. I know we enjoyed him and learned much from him.

He was the first of a long, long list of foreign visitors from all over the world, although, as I now recall, they came predominantly from Africa, the Orient and Asia. It disgusted me that there was no question of hotel accommodations for dark-skinned visitors in their native costumes, while those in American dress had to be housed in private homes. It occurred to me that all our Negroes needed to do to achieve equality of opportunity was to wrap a towel around their heads.

We set up a committee to arrange the entertainment of these foreign travelers, hoping this would prove to be a two way street. We wanted to explain our concern and our aims but also we wanted our women to have the experience of friendly association with members of the black and yellow races. Through these contacts, some of our members who were not entirely in favor of civil rights lessened their prejudices, and I hope we sent back with our visitors to their distant homes a more favorable impression of Little Rock.

Thus our program extended far afield. On the

night of February 3, a representative of a South American newspaper attended our open meeting at the Christ Church assembly room. It was a blustery, stormy night so we were all the more pleased to have a good audience. We showed a film of St. Louis' successful approach to desegregation "A City Decides," and we presented a panel to discuss the pertinence of this film to our local situation. This panel consisted of Ed Lester, as the M.C., Dr. Lewis Long, a psychologist whose wife had been an active member of our committee, the Rev. Wm. A. Willcox, Jr., pastor of St. Mark's Episcopal Church, J.O. Powell, Velma's husband, Dean of Men at Central High, and Chris Barrier, a displaced senior high school student. A number of our younger women were ushers. We had a display of propaganda material at the entrance door. I made a brief introductory speech. The panel discussion was frank, positive and informative. We felt the evening had import, but it had more than we bargained for. Within days, Dr. Long was dismissed from his position as psychologist at the state Hospital for Nervous Diseases. I talked with him and his wife. I prepared a protesting statement for the papers; they both felt it wiser that the WEC not enter the picture further in their behalf, as it might intensify reprisals on other known supporters of our committee.

During these months, the programs at our open meetings at Mrs. Terry's brought further inspiration and knowledge to an ever growing attendance. We were expanding in every way possible. One of our members called our attention to the subversive local program on radio called Party Line. Anyone was permitted to call in and express an opinion on anything and too often strident voices preached hate and anger. Many of us knew of this but it took Mrs. Allen to get us into high gear in combating it. She wrote me a letter:

I heard over the Party Line somebody complain that nearly all of the jobs were being given to colored people at the University of Arkansas, and that Mr. Joe Brewer was at the head of it. Then somebody called in and said, "Well, you know Mrs. Brewer is the head of that Women's Committee to Open Our Schools, so you see why that is, don't you?" I was afraid, not knowing any of the facts in the case, to call in and correct that opinion, but I sat there and wished that somebody who KNEW the FACTS would call in. I haven't heard anything on that Party Line but rabid haters and segregationists. I do wish that you women would appoint some people on your committee who are IN THE KNOW to "hog that line" every night, and in a gentle, patient way inform the people of something other than hate.

Not only did our women begin to jam the line with happy talk, but I went to discuss this program with the FBI. The officer to whom I talked was most attentive. He made copious notes, although I've no notion why or if he ever used them for any purpose. As I rose to go, he asked, "Have *you* ever been threatened?"

"Well," I told him with a smile, "people have warned me or my husband over the phone, or in anonymous letters, that I'd be dead before night, or have something horrible happen to me, but nobody had ever said pointedly, '*I* am going to kill *you.*'

"Well, then," he looked at me somberly, "if anything ever happens, let us know."

Six

AH MEN!

All of this winter and through the spring of 1959, we were heading toward another crisis, a major one. We had warnings of it as early as February. A *Gazette* reporter got wind of a threat to dismiss some of the Central High School teachers. The story was that in return for a purge, the Little Rock School Board could retrieve the state aid being withheld from the closed high schools. The report by the Superintendent to the Little Rock School Board indicated that the District would be $139,000 short of paying its February bills and probably would end the year about $200,000 in the red because of withheld state aid. At a press conference on February 10, Governor Faubus said he knew nothing of such a purge, but that if he were the one to say, he would not rehire Matthews, Principal of Central High, Mrs. Huckaby, Dean of Girls at Central, or J.O. Powell, Dean of Men there.

On February 6, we had sent a letter addressed to Mr. Ed I. McKinley, President of the School Board, with copies to each member of the Board, and we released it to the newspapers:

> We urge that you renew the contracts of the teachers in the four closed high schools without delay. Losing our present fine staff of teachers would be a blow to our public school system which Little Rock cannot afford. Retaining them is an obligation you owe to our children, our city and yourself. Our 1,040 members depend on you in this crisis.

But the contracts were not renewed. The School Board was split three to three on almost every question. The extremists' proposed solution to this impasse was to permit the governor, by legislation, to control the decisions of the Board by appointing three additional members. As this bill was killed, the Board became solidified three to three. Judge Laster said he would prefer to see the schools permanently abandoned rather than accept any degree of court-ordered integration. Ben D. Rowland, Sr. said he would be willing to keep the schools closed forever. It was assumed that Ed I. McKinley agreed with them since he consistently voted with them, and since he and the governor appeared to be in accord. How we rued the day we permitted his candidacy for the School Board to go unopposed.

Late in January the Board had petitioned the Federal Court to permit it to reopen the high schools segregated and allow them time to work out a new plan which would be acceptable to the public. The Department of Justice entered the case, asserting the Board was acting in bad faith. Judge Miller denied the Board's plea, adding laconically that they did not need permission from him to study a new plan.

In February, Judge Laster came up with a new idea. He suggested that the teachers' contracts include a clause stating they were hired to teach only in segregated schools, and providing that the contracts be null and void should they do otherwise. Thus, Mr. Laster reasoned, if the government forced integration, the schools might be integrated, all right, but they would have no teachers. Everett Tucker called a meeting of the Board to consider this plan. At the same time, he, Ted Lamb and Russell Matson issued a lengthy statement on the school situation which expressed their realization that there was no alternative to closed schools except open schools with controlled integration. Only these three put in an appearance at this called meeting, and lacking a quorum, they could do no more than issue a statement condemning the Laster plan.

Several times, we asked our friends on the School Board to meet with us to discuss specific developments or proposals. They were unfailingly cooperative in *listening* to us, but we often felt we were facing a blank wall. It became more and more evident that Ted Lamb was the only unflinching integrationist on the Board and we began to wonder about there being a moderate among the others.

Everett Tucker, a southern gentleman who typified the traditions of the old South, was forever courtly but was constantly imbued with segregationist prejudice. Not once did I phone him to ask for an appointment but he said immediately, "Where are you now? I'll come to see you." This I appreciated but I did wish for a change in his convictions. Russell Matson grew less and less affirmative in his anti-Faubus attitude. I was told this was due to the strong influence of his close friend, Herschel H. Friday, Jr., who handled all legal matters for the Little Rock School Board. Mr. Friday was a member of the firm of Mehaffy, Smith and Williams, hired by the School Board in December of 1958. This was a step which none of us in the WEC could understand, for this firm also represented Governor Faubus and Mr. Smith was the governor's foremost advisor. In fact, some thought him the authentic governor.

I asked Ted Lamb why he approved this appointment. "I thought what a joke it would be when the governor's own legal aides helped us reopen the schools," he explained with what I thought misplaced humor. But Ted Lamb proved to be our one unwavering friend on the School Board. We were to fight for his retention on it until he decided to resign in 1964 in order to attain a law degree with the intent of handling civil rights cases.

In justice to Mr. Friday, I should add that one of our members brought me a reassuring report from a conversation with him. He was not, Marguerite Henry was convinced, hampered by his firm. Most of his clients wanted public schools and he knew that Arkansas could not afford closed schools. Beyond that, he had confided that William Smith was not the instigator of the governor's actions, that it was Mr. Faubus himself who thought up his ideas regarding the school situation and surprisingly, at the moment, Faubus had no plans. We tried to take heart from this account but there were many times we wondered about its connotations.

As early as January 1959, Velma Powell gave to our executive committee a draft of suggestions to be presented to the School Board. She had put much time and thought into its preparation and all of us were grateful to be putting before the Board concrete suggestions concerning the desegregation of the Little Rock schools. The Board received these politely but that was the last we heard of them. Perhaps they remain in the School Board files? Even so, to show the trend of our thinking, they may be worth quoting:

SUGGESTIONS CONCERNING DESEGREGATION OF LITTLE ROCK SCHOOLS

1. To avoid having one school the focal point of pressure, we suggest the Board re-draw attendance area lines and desegregate all three white high schools.

   a. The Board should appoint a bi-racial advisory committee of community leaders representing all interested groups to assist the Board.

   b. As the governing agency involved, the Board should discuss its planned procedures positively and publicly and should enlist the assistance of all school personnel, community leadership, news media and the local police authorities to insure success. Once in effect, such procedures should be aggressively backed by all concerned. The Board should hold to the program regardless of opposition from pressure groups.

2. Establish and fill the position of Associate Superintendent. The Associate Superintendent would head a special office charged with directing and carrying out the desegregation program. Such a person should have wide general and professional knowledge and forcefulness and be willing to persevere in desegregating the schools to the best interests of the children and the community. Under the Associate Superintendent's supervision would be the following:

   a. To work out a plan with all news media for handling information relating to desegregation. (This might be the means of re-establishing rapport between the public schools and the community.)

b. To help the Board review and develop a firm policy on discipline and to work with various school administrators in setting up responsibilities in connection with disciplinary aspects of desegregation.

c. To help plan and coordinate efforts by PTA groups and related organizations interested in the success of the desegregation program.

d. To conduct workshops involving students, teachers, school secretaries and parents (using trained people in human relations and possibly in sociological aspects) to help clarify the procedures planned and to create a climate of acceptance. Set up definite policy regarding participation of Negro children in school activities.

e. To establish and maintain close liaison with community organizations interested in the overall welfare of Little Rock.

f. To establish and maintain close liaison with local law enforcement agencies.

g. To work out programs for preparing teachers, students and parents to work constructively in a desegregated school system.

   1. Teachers' meetings could be desegregated.

2. It might prove extremely helpful for the guidance departments of the Negro schools and the White schools to work together.

3. Students groups and student leaders should be used in every way possible in planning for and carrying out smooth desegregation within the schools.

4. Might set up exchange program where students and teachers could visit schools already desegregated.

5. Set up a reference library on desegregation and human relations in each school for use of teachers, students and parents and encourage use of such a library.

h. The Associate Superintendent might work with various groups in the community on such projects as:

1. Discussing the Supreme Court's decision.

2. Studying community benefits of desegregation.

3. Compiling answers to most asked questions about the racial problem.

4. Printing booklet describing the Little Rock desegregation plan and how it will be implemented.

5. Getting endorsements from citizens and organizations for the plan.

6. Making a survey of present status of desegregation in the community.

In April, Mr. Ed McCuiston, the Assistant Education Commissioner, and the state NCA committee requested the withdrawal of accreditation of Central and Hall High Schools by the North Central Accrediting Association. Their argument was that the schools, when reopened, would have an easier chance of regaining accreditation. This we could not buy and we wished more of our adversaries would read and heed the editorial in the *Arkansas Gazette* from which I quote:

> The tangled tale of the resignation from the North Central Association of Colleges and Secondary Schools by the Little Rock high schools is another example of the sad state of public education in this city and in Arkansas. It was done without consultation with the officials of the Little Rock School District, and in violation of their wishes as expressed in formal documents delivered to Mr. McCuiston's office. Here again the state has simply usurped the authority and prerogatives normally reserved to the local school districts. And here again this has been done with calm arrogance and without even the pretense of consultation and consent. All of which raises the suspicion that the NCA maneuver may be part of a larger design to permanently undercut the Little Rock public schools in favor of the private system, which may come into being if court desegregation orders are extended to the lower grades. This will be true even if the association's standards can be met, under regulations that apply to all new schools, public and private. Thus, if this

action had not been taken, there would have been a chance that unaccredited Raney would have found itself in competition with accredited Central and Hall — a matter of some moment to those students who plan to go to college. Whether this was in fact the motive in the present case, the fact is that at least three members of the School Board, and Governor Faubus, are on record with their willingness to dismantle the public school system of Little Rock rather than permit any degree of court-ordered integration. A long step in that direction will be taken in the next few weeks if the three pro-Faubus Board members succeed in their effort to prevent renewal of contracts for the high school teachers.

Through this winter and spring, members of one of our subcommittees had made a systematic effort to strengthen the morale of the teachers who daily faced their empty classrooms, by visiting and talking with them, by having lunch with them. In late April, Tucker, Lamb and Matson disclosed that they, too, had been visiting the schools, lunching with the teachers and advising them that there was every reason to believe that the high schools would be open in the fall. Yet, on April 29, a survey made by school authorities for the School Board and Superintendent Terrell E. Powell revealed that the Little Rock School District was faced with the prospect of replacing 165 teachers for the coming fall. Already, 121 had resigned and forty-four probably would do so. In the preceding year, the departures totaled only sixty. Of the 165 resignations (out of 828 teachers) only eleven were presented by Negro teachers; 154 were from white teachers. Superintendent Powell pointed out that 154 was thirteen more than the total faculties of the three high schools for white students.

There was little doubt that Act 10 of 1958 had something to do with this. Act 10 was the Teacher Affidavit Law, providing that every teacher, superintendent and principal employed by schools supported even in part by public funds must file an affidavit as to his or her membership in or contributions to every organization within the last five years. This was ruled constitutional on its face by the Arkansas Supreme Court, and this decision was supported in early June by the three judge Federal Court at the same time it ruled Act 115 of 1959, barring NAACP members from public employment in the state, unconstitutional. Governor Faubus spoke of Act 10 as a moderate, liberal and tolerant law, but teachers in the public schools and professors in the University and the state Colleges disagreed. The growing threat to the University of Arkansas was propounded by Mr. Hardy Wilcoxon, professor of psychology, in speaking of the dilemma facing every thoughtful educator in Arkansas:

> Act 10 is a bad law, and I am convinced that if it remains in force over the years, it will do great damage to the University and all other educational institutions in Arkansas...If I sign, it will be because I came to the conclusion that the best way to rid ourselves of the thing is to sign and stay rather than refuse to sign and leave. Act 10 is not the first piece of recent legislation

that has been designed to harass and, if possible, drive out of the state, the kind of teacher we must retain if Arkansas is ever to re-emerge from the combination of natural fog and deliberately-laid smokescreen which now obscures our collective thinking. Any substantial movement on the part of the University of Arkansas faculty members to oppose Act 10 will automatically make the University the Number One target of the forces of anti-education, but this fate was inevitable anyway. There have always been people standing around waiting for an opportunity to give it to the University between the ribs. It is only lately, however, that these forces have had such high-placed and powerful friends. The Medical School had been the first to feel the really severe pressure, possibly because it is located at Little Rock, and therefore affords a close target for critics in the state government; the main campus at Fayetteville has been next in line, possibly because it is so far away and nobody inside the state government can be entirely sure that "they" aren't turning out informed electors up there. Finally, the University is the closest thing to the educational ideal of a "Community of Scholars" that the state of Arkansas has yet seen, and for that reason alone must have its enemies, particularly in times such as the present.

The University of Arkansas professors were in an uproar of protest against the law. The Dean of the University made a strong speech against it. A group of professors at Arkansas Tech volunteered to join with the University of Arkansas faculty in opposing Act 10. Everywhere among the educators there was unrest and rebellion. The Act came very close to the home of the WEC. Velma's husband J.O. Powell, Dean of Men at Central High, adamantly refused to sign an affidavit. He willingly gave the press a list of his affiliations with, and contributions to, organizations but he refused to sign the list before a notary. This demand affronted his sense of American freedom so much that even when the act was at last declared unconstitutional, he refused to consider staying in the Little Rock school system; by one phone call he secured a position in a California high school and before fall, he moved himself, Velma and their goods and chattels out of our state. The loss of Velma to our executive board was a serious one.

One of the WEC ads in the Little Rock papers during this time read bluntly: "People who care about their teachers, their children's education, their city's future, want open public schools." We were then running one advertisement each week and mailing out a new flyer every other week. Mr. Philip Back, owner of a Public Relations business, the husband of one of our members, was generous in helping us develop designs and procure drawings and plates. I remember well: "Political football, anyone?" depicting footballs labeled teachers' contracts, school money, public education. We were stepping up all of our activities. Following the recess of the legislature, we wrote unnumbered letters to the legislators who had stood for public education. One of our young members, the editor of a hospital news sheet, wrote for us a "Letter from Little Rock" which we sent to out-of-state friends who might use it to acquaint their friends and organizations with the activities of the WEC. I was calling on all business men and ministers who would receive me, asking their help to re-open the schools, ever hoping for public statements and possible formation of pro-education groups among the members of the power structure. Members of the WEC had been attending all School Board meetings, trying to encourage the three "moderate" members, assuring them they were not forgotten men. We were sending speakers to any club which would consent to give us even a very few moments on their program. I was especially pleased when Mrs. L.M. McGoodwin of Fayetteville, president of the state board of the AAUW, invited me to speak before their meeting on April 17 in the Colonial Room of the Hotel Marion in Little Rock. And I was delighted that she allocated a half hour to enable me to brief the WEC's program and to have a question and answer session.

Through Mrs. Guerdon D. Nichols, representing a group of concerned women, chiefly members or wives of members of the faculty at the University of Arkansas, had come the invitation to speak at a luncheon on the same Saturday when Harry Ashmore was to make the address at the banquet meeting of the Blue Key. My trip to Fayetteville on May 2nd was memorable for many reasons. Joe drove me there, and I put together my talk during the ride, my first opportunity to collect my wits for that. There were 127 men and women at the luncheon and it was the first time Joe had ever heard me make a public speech. I told of the work of the WEC, but I concentrated on the laws threatening public education and the dangers which menaced every school in the entire state. I asked for a rising vote of congratulations and appreciation for Dr. Nichols who had publicly and with great personal risk attacked the infamous Act No. 10. I warned that there were rumors there might be another special session of the legislature before the summer's end. The response was flattering and heartening, and there was encouragement financially. I took my greatest hope from a story which came to me that night. One of the women in the audience had come from the governor's own bailiwick to hear what I had to say. She told a Fayetteville acquaintance that since her family and the Faubus family had a long-standing friendship, she had shut her ears and mind to his pronouncements in the Little Rock school controversy but now, although it made her very sad, she had to admit he was wrong.

Following the banquet that evening, at which Harry Ashmore spoke brilliantly, Dean and Mrs. Nichols entertained at a cocktail supper. There Harry was completely surrounded, as an oracle, by professors and their wives. It was not until very late in the evening that I joined this circle, for I had chanced to meet again Hal Douglas, Bill Fulbright's brother-in-law, whom we had known in Washington days. For nearly an hour I discussed with him Bill's silence in the Little Rock situation, and I thought Hal was ready to advise Bill that it was time to take a vigorous, vocal stand for public education and law and order in his home state. Then we turned to listen to Harry just as he was saying that he had told Bill to maintain his silence on the crisis in Little Rock. As I recall, Harry's reasoning ran something like this: Bill was now the third man in the federal hierarchy, chairman of the Foreign Relations Committee in the U.S. Senate. If he stayed clear of the controversy, he was sure to become the second man, the Secretary of State. How could my opinion hope to compete with Harry's in Hal's estimation? Certainly it could not in Bill's. Greatly disturbed, I said, "Harry, I've always listened to you and I always shall, but for this once, I can not agree with you one iota." No one else sided with me openly, although I was told later that some did secretly. It does not make me happy that time proved me right.

Our weekly ads continued: "Will this be your child next fall?" (drawing depicted student with suitcase in hand.) "Over 1,000 children had to leave Little Rock to go to school this year. There is no substitute for Public Schools. All citizens must be educated to preserve our Democracy. History has proved: Public schools are necessary for educating the majority. Only a few can be educated in private schools. Clear thinkers know that we cannot afford two school systems. Tax money cannot support two school systems. How much will your children's education cost you? Public schools are supported by all tax payers. Private schools are supported by parents. Good private schools cost parents as much as college. SPEAK OUT FOR PUBLIC SCHOOLS."

As customary, the WEC continued to hold its monthly open meetings at Mrs. Terry's home. These were well attended and brought us informative speakers. I recall that the former president of the School Board, Wayne Upton, spoke to us in January, bringing us a clear picture of the developments before the resignation of his Board. After the legislature adjourned, Bob Shults spoke, explaining our confusing galaxy of laws, and encouraging us that our work was beginning to make an impact on the public.

On May 5th, we held our regular open meeting to hear the story of the efforts of the early settlers to establish free public education for all of the children in Arkansas, but I heard none of it. Many of our members were monitoring the School Board meeting that afternoon and the phone rang constantly, bringing increasingly agitated messages. At the close of our program, my voice shook with emotion as I startled the WEC. "They are firing our teachers right and left." We immediately cast a unanimous vote in support of our teachers and adjourned with the promise that reports would be made to every member.

The following morning, Ted Lamb came to our executive committee meeting to explain what had happened. The Little Rock School Board had met to consider teacher contracts for 1959-1960. Tucker,

Matson and Lamb had voted to approve all the contracts recommended by the superintendent, but McKinley, Laster and Rowland refused to go along with this. The split was its usual three to three, and at noon, Tucker, Matson and Lamb walked out, believing this would prevent a quorum and consequently nothing could be done. The "Faubus group" refusing to be circumvented, proceeded to reject the contracts of forty-four employees: seven principals, three secretaries and thirty-four teachers. Before sundown, the Little Rock Classroom Teachers Association had called this action illegal, but this did not move the three extremists. Feelings ran high, as Harry Ashmore's editorial well illustrates:

> It was a day that saw the first, broad public reaction against the reckless course of government or Faubus and his supporters. Always before the issue had been blurred by emotion and official doubletalk, and the prospect of disaster was offset by the springing of hope. But now there was no longer any reason to doubt that the only issue was whether or not we shall continue to have public schools in this city. The collision course launched more than a year and a half ago by Mr. Faubus had come to an inevitable climax. And here, finally in the open, was the matter of whether or not the organized extremist groups in the city could dominate this public agency, and in the end all others, through coercion and intimidation.

The Little Rock PTA Council, vocal at last, adopted a statement of strong criticism of the firing of the teachers, as all 44 dismissed employees came to be called, and suggested consideration of recall proceedings. Promoted by PTA members, mass protest meetings against the purge were held at six elementary and junior high schools, and at one, recall petitions against the three pro-Faubus members of the School Board were started. The WEC phone chain had moved into prompt action to assure large attendance at these meetings, and from that day until the victory party, this chain worked tirelessly and effectively. To Jane Mendel, organizer and captain of this chain of communication, and of an additional chain of STOP members, goes much of the credit for the success of the recall election, indubitably one of the most important events in the history of Little Rock.

Governor Faubus seemed unperturbed. "It might be better," he opined, "to just recall all six members of the School Board and see how it comes out. I've said before that I never object to elections." *Gazette* editorials reported that the former school teacher, Orval Faubus, had said that when he was fired by a Madison County School Board, he just went out and found another job, and the people in the school district didn't rise up and demand the recall of the School Board members. Commented the *Gazette* with pointed irony, "176 Little Rock school district teachers had found other jobs without being fired."

Now, *mirabile dictu*, a number of men were sufficiently aroused to move out into the light of day. On the afternoon of Friday, May 8, approximately 179 prominent business and civic leaders met in the auditorium of the Union National Bank. Ed Lester had told Irene Samuel and me of this scheduled meeting and while there was no invitation, we decided to go. Averted glances as we entered the hall made it very clear that we were *personae non gratae.* A few of the men whom we knew best hastened to turn their backs to avoid speaking. As the meeting progressed, STOP (Stop This Outrageous Purge) was organized with Dr. Drew Agar as chairman. There followed a discussion of groups they hoped to involve in the campaign to recall McKinley, Laster and Rowland. The WEC was conspicuously absent from the list, and Dr. John Samuel made bold to rise and add our name. There was an enormous silence which spoke like thunder. Afterwards, Dr. Samuel puzzled, "What was the matter with them?" and Irene smiled ruefully, "They just don't want to be identified with us." *But they wanted our help; how they wanted our help!* They made that plain without delay. At least they wanted all but mine. "You go home and stay there, Vivion," Ed Lester advised me. "Your being known in this will only hurt us." That hurt me, but I accepted his verdict that my name had become an invitation to incendiary screams, "Integration!" and *that* we did not need.

Immediately, our already crowded office became the center for hurried, excited men offering advice, directing plans, supplying badly needed equipment: typewriters, chairs, telephones, a mimeograph machine. Reporters and photographers filed in and out, assuming this to be the STOP headquarters, ignoring the WEC staff. Who cared? To have men taking a public stand was what we had been working for and we listened with renewed hope when W.S. Mitchell, a prominent attorney, went on TV to plead with the governor, "Let us alone. Let us return our community to a rule of reason."

Although for the most part, the WEC was the underground, our women never worked harder. Irene Samuel swung into action with her compulsive drive and with the constant advice of Henry Woods whose long experience had made him wise in the mechanics of politics. Our goal was enough but our ardor was fanned by an extremist group organized as CROSS (Committee to Retain Our Segregated Schools) which was chaired by the Reverend M.L. Moser, Jr., and supported by the Capital Citizens Council, the States Rights Council and the Mothers League of Central High School. CROSS was circulating petitions to recall Tucker, Matson and Lamb.

Both sides entered upon a vigorous campaign, using radio, TV and newspaper ads. The WEC ran two large advertisements in the papers:

Citizens of Little Rock, have you had enough?
SAVE OUR TEACHERS.

Now is the time for all good men
to come to the aid of the teachers.

Anne Helvenston directed the use of materials from the National Citizens Council for Better Schools. Volunteers jammed the office. Countless women circulated petitions and established centers over the city where signatures could be notarized. Women worked days and nights checking signatures against poll books to assure acceptance of the petitions. Twenty young women were at the County Court House Tuesday morning at 8:45 to help publicize the filing of our petitions.

A messenger service functioned from 8:00 a.m. through 6:00 p.m. daily to secure supplies, to deliver materials. Fifty-four women armed with poll books, city directories and criss-cross directories typed cards on the 1400 WEC members, the 211 STOP members and many others known to be friendly. In time, more volunteers in day and night shifts catalogued the entire poll book, particularly identifying the signers of the STOP and of the CROSS petitions, noting the ward and precinct numbers on each card.

Our staff secured the consent of teachers to have their pictures used in "This teacher was purged" ads, and found forty people to appear on TV spots: prominent men and women graduates of Central High School; ministers; doctors; business men; in every case, persons who had no known association with the WEC. A nightly news sheet was deemed valuable as boosters for all STOP members and precinct workers, and this STOPLIGHT was mimeographed in our office and mailed by our women, sometimes as late as 1 a.m. A rally honoring all of the high school teachers was planned for Tuesday night, May 19, and not only did the staff provide our own Jo Jackson one of the speakers for the program, but through letters, telegrams, our telephone chain and personal contact, assured a large and enthusiastic audience.

From files so tediously assembled during the winter and spring, the WEC prepared lists of suggested judges, clerks and poll watchers for each precinct, and obtained agreement from each person listed to serve if called by the election commission. Ward liaison personnel, ward chairmen, precinct chairmen, court reporters were found. Motor pools were set up in all areas. Ward meetings were arranged, mimeographed information on organization and procedure was supplied to each worker. The poll list cards were delivered to proper precincts, with corps of telephone workers appointed in each section. On May 25, *the day,* constant communication with all workers and every precinct was maintained. Many weak spots were strengthened and trouble spots corrected.

But CROSS had been busy, too, and in one ad was rash enough to suggest that immorality was one of the reasons for the purge of the teachers. Indignant, to put it mildly, thirty-nine of the purged teachers filed a $3,900,000 libel suit against Mr. Moser and Mr. McKinley, a suit which dragged on and on until it was finally dismissed in 1962.

Mr. Faubus entered the fight with an emotional defense of the McKinley three-some, trying as always to set class against class, race against race, calling the STOP workers "the Cadillac brigade," adding "with the good, honest, hardworking Negroes in the front as shock troops." For the first time he attacked me personally. So much for Ed Lester's precaution.

Joe and I sat alone in our living room on Friday, May 22, deeply depressed by Joe's having been demoted suddenly and without explanation to *assistant* personnel officer at the Veterans Administration Hospital. Although we should have been forewarned by this change in Joe's status, we were shocked to hear the governor proclaim in his rasping voice, "These are the leaders in the Little Rock controversy: Mrs. Joe Brewer, president of the Women's Emergency Committee, who has no children and who does not even live in the Little Rock school district. She is the wife of a federal employee at the Veterans Hospital facility Fort Roots. How does she justify her so active role in the school affairs of the city in which she does not even live?" He then attacked Joe Hardin, vice president of the Arkansas Louisiana Gas Company, who lived at Grady and was a Catholic. Mr. Hardin had made a talk for public schools at the STOP city-wide Teacher Appreciation Rally at the auditorium. The governor continued: "Last week it was reported Mrs. Grace Lorch returned by private plane to Little Rock for conference. She is the person who attended, as an official delegate, a state communist convention in a New England state and was active in the Little Rock affair in 1957. These are strange allies indeed! And strange that they should be found on the same side in this controversy here!"

I did not know Mrs. Lorch but I made wide inquiry and if she were in Little Rock at that time, I could not so ascertain. A few days after this at a chance meeting, I asked Mr. Hardin if he were as flattered as I by being mentioned publicly by the governor. He looked very somber and shook his head. "No," he told me, "I'm worried." The August 29, 1959 issue of the *Arkansas Gazette* carried a news item, stating in part:

JOE HARDIN RESIGNS POST WITH ARKLA

Hardin's announced reason for resigning was his desire to devote full time to personal affairs. Hardin also took an active role earlier this year in the Little Rock school integration controversy, a role that was on the opposite side from that of Governor Faubus, one of whose principal financial supporters has been W.R. Stephens, President and Board Chairman of ArkLa. Hardin could not be reached at his Grady home yesterday for comment on his resignation, which was announced by ArkLa's public relations staff at Shreveport.

The developments in the lives of Joe and myself seemed to bear a close association with the governor's attack also.

Following the Faubus speech that night, I was sure our phone would ring, but there was not one call. Both my friends and my enemies were too busy, or too tired. Was it possible we had had a bad dream? I phoned the WEC office and a masculine voice answered. It was Jim Youngdahl, working very late on one of the STOPLIGHTS for the campaign.

"Are any of the WEC members there?" I asked, for at that time I did not know Jim.

"No, they've all gone."

"Did you hear Faubus?"

"Yes."

"Did you hear his attack on the WEC?"

"Yes."

"Well, good luck," I said lamely. At least I now knew we had not dreamed that outrageous innuendo.

In the third week of April, KKK activity came to light in Little Rock and the surrounding county. Several hundred or more cards soliciting KKK membership were placed in different parts of the city, and on election eve, klan posters were seen throughout the area. Governor Faubus again addressed the TV audience, assuring it that the purge of the teachers was a side issue, that the real issue was integration versus segregation. But the tide had begun to turn. May 25 is history. STOP won the election by a narrow margin, but won! We had retained our three members on the School Board and had ousted the pro-Faubus three.*

About seven that election night, Irene Samuel phoned, excited, optimistic. She was near one of the precincts where she had been checking and "Now

---

* The story of those frenzied days has been ably detailed for the Eagleton Institute of Politics as Case 17: The Little Rock Recall Election by Dr. Henry M. Alexander, Professor of Government at the University of Arkansas.

the men want me to come down to the hotel for a while." That evening turned into a celebration but it was the May 26 *Gazette* which brought me the first news of the victory party at the hotel the night before. It was STOP's night.

However, many were aware of the indispensable role played by the WEC. There were numerous heartening letters. One letter from the ten members of the administration office staff of the Little Rock Public Schools read:

Dear Mrs. Brewer:

This is a new day in a new Little Rock and we feel wonderful about it all.

We are sincerely grateful to you for being a part of the whole that has made it possible for us once again to hold our heads high.

From this day forward, we hope we can work toward making Little Rock schools second to none, and help our beautiful city achieve its rightful place.

With deepest appreciation, we are

    Most sincerely,

There was one from Mrs. Huckaby, the Dean of Girls at Little Rock Central High School:

Dear Mrs. Brewer:

Although the major credit for turning the tide in Little Rock will generally be assigned to the dramatic STOP, that organization could not have been successful in turning us toward reasonableness

---

> if the Women's Emergency Committee had not been at work for so many months, defending the schools, educating the public, and assembling the workers who were so effective in STOP.
>
> Thank you for all you have done: the moral support you have offered the teachers, the excellent propaganda you have presented for public schools, your sponsorship of moderate school board candidates, and your legislative efforts which helped block the "purge" in February. And, since the high schools are still closed, I hope that your group, with the added support that STOP has gathered, will not lessen your efforts to Open Our Schools.
>
> With sincere thanks to you and to your organization...

A letter to the *Editor of the Gazette* from three men at the Arkansas Industrial Research Center was published by the paper:

> Accolades have been passed out right and left to loyal fighters in the STOP campaign. To our minds, far too little homage has been paid the Women's Emergency Committee to Open Our Schools. By initially defining the only problem with which Little Rock can at present effectively cope — opening the schools, by demonstrating that an organization could be formed and held together to wage this fight and by performing much of the "hard labor" connected with the campaign itself, the Women's Committee contributed more to STOP's victory than has been publicly recognized to date.
>
> Ralph Gray, Winston C. Beard,
> William T. Greenwood.

There were many letters from teachers, and a delightful one from the Reverend Will D. Campbell, which I quote in part:

> Dear St. Vivion of Little Rock,
>
> I have rejoiced, as I am sure you have, that various elements have found it too crowded behind the scenes (where so many of us like to work) and have decided to move out a bit. It seems that you have been successful in accomplishing some of the things you were working on when I saw you last. Good operation! Let not the Saints say they have beaten down our adversary, the devil, but let them delight in this present victory, and let all the people say AMEN. Or perhaps, Ah, Men, it's about time.

The men of STOP were frank to admit that they could never have got off the ground had it not been for the efficient organization of the WEC. They simply could not have functioned, for they had no means of securing the necessary information and the volunteers on such short notice. It should be pointed out that the men of STOP furnished the money for the campaign, without which the WEC could not have accomplished all it did. It was a most gratifying co-operation and the WEC was saddened as STOP, like old soldiers, faded quietly away. But as STOP vanished, it presented to the WEC the additional equipment which it had had to assemble in our office in order that the women might turn out the letters, the mimeographed sheets, the long lists, the files of cards, all the details of the campaign — and so we became two-time winners.

Seven

On To Victory

Just before the recall election we moved our office because Dr. and Mrs. Kolb needed their room for the summer months. We found a small space on the second floor of a building owned by one of our members in a shopping development nearer the homes of most of our workers. We asked that our original phone number be saved for the WEC and the telephone company obliged. This was a bit of luck, for most of our members had memorized our number. Our rent was only $20 per month, and the location was so much more convenient for most of our women that I accepted without objection the daily forty mile drive in my Corvair between the office and my home. That was forty miles when I made no detours for necessary calls, which often added ten to thirty miles to my routine trip. To this new place, up a narrow, steep stairway on the second floor, most of our women could hurry over from their domestic duties in their casual clothes, and as the hot summer progressed, I envied them their short journeys as well as their abbreviated attire. Never sure what a day would bring for me, I had to be dressed for visitors, and often I felt wilted from my long hot drive. I was, therefore, most grateful when Mr. James Binder installed an air conditioner for us in that stifling room.

Our first concern after the successful recall election was the little-known, although elected, Pulaski County Board of Education. Only one of this five man group lived in Little Rock; two of the five were reported to be strong Faubus supporters. These five now had the authority to name the replacements for the three recalled members of the School Board. We were worried about this and made an effort to reach all five with suggestions of names of citizens who would support our schools. However, this Board would not give us more satisfaction than the assurance that they had made an agreement to appoint no one who did not have the unanimous endorsement of the five. Mr. Faubus' remark that he did not feel the results of Monday's recall election indicated the people of Little Rock wanted him to keep hands off their public school affairs did not soothe us. Anxiously we awaited June 11 and the announcement of the three new members of the Little Rock School Board. They were J.H. Cottrell, a state representative we were advised to trust and who in time became a county campaign manager for Mr. Faubus (!); B. Frank Mackey, an insurance man who eventually became the County Judge, and was a friend of H.L. Thomas, who had unsuccessfully submitted to the governor his own plan for reopening the schools; and H.L. Hubbard, who was immediately disqualified from taking his place on the Board and was quickly replaced by W.C. McDonald, the manager of Western Paper Co., who pleased us with his first public statement: "I believe in public education and I believe our schools should be opened in spite of our feelings about integration and segregation."

The new Little Rock School Board went to work on June 16. The actions taken by the recalled members at that infamous May meeting were expunged from the record, and all the contracts of the teachers were renewed, excepting only those who had refused to sign affidavits under Act 10 and who therefore could not be re-appointed legally. Mr. Terrell Powell was re-hired as Superintendent of the Little Rock schools. On June 18, the three-judge Federal Court overruled the Arkansas Supreme Court and determined that School Closing Act 4 and State Aid Transfer Act 5 were unconstitutional. Both days brought cause for rejoicing, but our elation was tempered by the great unrest and continuing fear of violence in the city. In his shrewd and reckless course, Mr. Faubus announced that he probably would appeal the decisions on Acts 4 and 5 to the United States Supreme Court and predicted that if the schools were opened mixed, there would be trouble, and again the use of federal force.

The minutes from a final meeting of the STOP organization, which invited the WEC to attend, give a lively evaluation of some of our worries and problems. I no longer recall who made these notes, but they were entered in our STOP file for future reference. Obviously these were notes jotted down at the meeting, later typed but not checked for syntax or punctuation:

NOTES FROM MEETING JULY 2, THURSDAY, COACH ROOM, MARION HOTEL

Mr. Will Mitchell gave a brief welcoming talk and discussed the success of the STOP campaign. Attributed it primarily to Timing (firing of the teachers) and Organization (use of the card system).

He pointed up the fact that there are approximately 5,000 to 6,000 Negro poll tax holders. 4,000 voted — almost everyone for STOP. Students from Shorter College helped drive cars in Negro areas and employers released their Negro employees between 1 and 2 to vote.

He introduced Mr. Maurice Mitchell who gave a brief analysis of the last election and pointed out that 30% of the vote went for Mrs. Stephens in the previous election but that 40% voted for STOP. The vote in the 5th ward was 2.2 to 1. A poll taken prior to the election showed STOP would lose most of the voters above 55 years. According to Mr. Mitchell this was borne out in Ward 5. Laster recalled by 2700 votes — without the Negro vote, the election would have gone the other way.

Mr. Will Mitchell said "A lot of missionary work is yet to be done in Little Rock to convince the people we must have public schools."

Mr. Victor Ray said that he and Mr. Kimberly are tremendously encouraged by the situation within Labor ranks. STOP gained ten to 15% of the vote in the union wards. This gives courage to leaders who believe in public schools. He announced a meeting Sunday, July 12, to form a Labor Committee to Preserve Public Schools.

A discussion was held on why it was not deemed advisable for the school board to file an appeal on Acts 4 and 5.

In answer to the question, "What can keep the schools from opening?," Mr. Mitchell said that any party has the right to ask the judges of the lower court for a "stay." If the stay is granted, the decision would remain as it is, but the effect would be the postponement of the opening date of school. If the lower Federal Court refuses to grant a stay, any *one* of the members of the Supreme Court can be petitioned to grant a stay. No one believes either Court would grant a stay. If the lawyers are correct, it means that come September, the school board is under a mandate from the courts to open the schools.

To the question, "Why should the school board join Gov. Faubus in an appeal?," Mr. Mitchell answered...they would simply be going along to show the entire population that it has nothing to hide and it is willing for the Supreme Court to pass on these acts.

When asked, "Could the Supreme Court meet in Special Session?," the answer was...the situation is completely reversed from last September. There is nothing to prompt the Supreme Court to do that under these facts. The Justice Department has indicated the court would not come back into special session.

It was stated that we must have loads of publicity

about the schools' opening. There should be a lot of enthusiasm from parents and pupils. Someone asked when they were going to prosecute the people responsible for the circulars that were passed out regarding the Negroes coming to the rally. The cases of the two Negroes have been postponed. Even tho' they have proved the stencil for the circular was cut on Laster's typewriter, the Prosecuting Attorney fears they would be taking a chance at this time to try to prove his responsibility — and they may make a martyr of him and he might win the Traffic Judge election.

When Mr. Mitchell asked for suggestions from those attending the meeting, Dr. Jerome Levy said, "We have won a battle and yet we haven't won a war. Who then can answer the governor? Who can say something to make the people realize that this will hurt their pocketbooks? We should get figures from over the country on the cost of private schools. We should propagandize. We should wring their hearts about the misplaced children of third-term Faubus. The Chamber of Commerce should put those facts before the people. They should bombard the people with the information as to what it is costing us to have our children go to private schools. Direction of this publicity might fall on the WEC. Direct our information to the particular organization which is proper. We should have a planned program shooting both barrels of propaganda to the people as to what it means to have the schools closed. If we get public opinion aroused, the school board will find it easy. We should emphasize the economic, ethical and moral loss of keeping these schools closed."

Dr. Sam Thompson said, "We should plan a coordinated group — some kind of a group. Through the WEC and the other organizations in this city, we can coordinate a policy committee to carry out our program. It should have one name with the men working, too."

Mrs. S.J. Field suggested that it would be helpful if the school authorities could hear from the parents to know that the parents and the school board are behind them all the way and the first instance of any difficulty would be handled immediately. Principals should work with parents. Could the PTAs meet before school opens? Could we have registration early?

Mr. Mitchell stated that registration is planned for about the first week in August, which is early compared to former years. It is planned to have exchange visits by the school board between Little Rock and recently integrated schools. We are planning to give out this information as soon as possible.

Pat House asked if we could have an excuse to have a large meeting? Mrs. Terry asked when someone is going to sue for the money turned over to Raney? ($71,905.50) Mr. Mitchell said what we need is harmony and we should postpone all suits. She also suggested that one-hundred young men go down and be sworn in as deputies and asked how do you go about getting sworn in.

Mrs. Reynolds suggested parties out in the neighborhoods bringing people up to date. Some discussion was held regarding the use of the precinct organizations for such discussion groups. Dr. Cowling said that "information is inspiration," and suggested coke parties. Miss Hildegarde Smith felt that neighborhood meetings would be valuable. We could assure the people the schools will be opened next fall. Positive steps should be taken so that there will be peace and harmony on that date. We should prepare propaganda to dispel rabble rousing propaganda.

Mrs. Malakoff asked, "Are there any political analysts who could tell us what the current financial support for Raney and any other private school is?" The answer was no.

Mrs. Fields suggested a questionnaire should be prepared for a neighborhood group. Mr. Mitchell said the people there know the questions that are in the people's minds. They should be presented to the school board so they can be certain they have the answers.

Mrs. Johnston said that it is a time for responsible people to refute Faubus' lies. Some man said, "That is what Cherry did."

Dr. Thompson said that an organization has to be developed. Some thought should be given to it as to how it should be put together. Maybe we should have a men's auxiliary to the WEC.

Mr. Joe Hardin suggested that we assure the school board that we are all for public schools — also teachers, superintendent and principals. Mr. Mitchell said ideas for the name of an organization should be forthcoming.

Dr. Cowling said that public schools are morally right and we would win out in the end, and closed the meeting with a prayer.

At the conclusion of this meeting, I had a brief conversation with Mr. Mitchell and was stunned to hear him say, "I think it is time for the leadership of all the interested groups to change. We ought to have all new names before the public." Evidently, I thought, he was trying to tell me I was doing more harm than good and I took this sobering advice home to ponder long and somewhat bitterly. But I decided that I had too much at stake to quit then. I simply could not give Mr. Faubus that satisfaction. Besides, I wanted to accomplish what I had set out to accomplish and I could never do that without an organization. Determined to carry on, I mentioned my quandary to no one. Instead I concentrated on pulling our organization together. The women were tired from the exhausting work of the STOP campaign and inclined to feel an understandable lassitude. But they rebounded quickly.

We initiated another membership drive, contacting the wife of every STOP signer who was not on our mailing list. A battery of women worked days correcting that mailing list. Some of the leaders of STOP decided to maintain a liaison with us and we set up a committee to meet with a few men each week. "But please," these men pleaded, "no hint ever of integration. Our group was too divided on this issue." We sent out a summertime news letter on *pink* paper and I am surprised that no one picked up on our use of that color (see Appendix 4).

The response convinced us a monthly newsletter was worth the expense. And what about ads? We were still running one a week, and they were not cheap, but so far we had been lucky about funds. Surprisingly enough, donations had come from as far away as Oregon, New York, California, Michigan, Arizona, Massachusetts, Washington, D.C. The National Council of Churches had generously sent us $300. Almost daily there were checks in our mail from local sympathizers, mostly small ones, but occasionally sizable ones. In May there was a devastating fire at the Negro detention home. Shortly after this, Bishop Robert R. Brown delivered $100 to us, a gift from an anonymous firm, obviously moved to consider racial inequities in all state institutions including schools. So we remained solvent and continued to try to use our funds wisely.

On June 24, a letter came from Mr. Herbert L. Thomas, the civic leader:

Dear Mrs. Brewer

I have been a contributor to and an admirer of your Committee. I think you have furnished the spark that has kept the moderates of Little Rock together in behalf of our schools. With this compliment, I now want to make a criticism which I hope is constructive.

I think the ad in today's paper, or any further ads under present conditions, are and would be damaging to our cause. The courts have said that the Governor cannot close our schools. The School Board has said they will be opened in September. I think the vast majority of our people have accepted that as a fact, and therefore it is my thinking that the less we say publicly that could irritate anybody, the more quietly we could work, (if

---

the other side will permit us), the more successful the school opening will be.

It is my belief that this morning's ad made no
new friends and would irritate the extreme segregationists and possibly the Governor. I am inclined to think it has the tendency to make them
want to put an ad in the paper saying, "Do not
permit the opening of our public schools on an
integrated basis."

I am inclined to think that it causes some people
who were thinking that it was a settled fact that
the schools were going to open, to wonder if they
really are.

I favor that all organizations think hard and be
prepared for any move the extreme segregationists make — but don't do anything unless we have
to.

I have today heard others express the same opinion, and I would appreciate your Committee
weighing the criticism in the spirit it is given.

Sincerely,

Herbert L. Thomas

Through an intermediary, we learned that Mr.
Thomas' wife thought we should now disband, and
the attitudes of these two prominent citizens shocked
us into a total re-evaluation of our program, which
only served to lead to further activities. My answer
to Mr. Thomas read:

Thank you for writing to us. Indeed we do appreciate the interest and support which prompt your suggestions and I assure you I have given much thought to your letter and our executive committee will carefully consider your advice when we meet on Wednesday.

I feel we owe it to you now, whatever we may then decide, to tell you we have already contracted for one more ad, which will run in the *Gazette* and the *Democrat* on Friday, July 3.

We certainly have no intention or desire to irritate anybody. Rather it is our hope, and we believe we must do what we can, to influence public opinion to support our public school system, not only to get our schools open but to keep them open. We'd like very much to be assured that the majority of Little Rock's citizens believe our public high schools will be open in September. I'm deeply sorry to say my own impression of public opinion in Little Rock is not so optimistic. That over 1,000 students have registered for attendance at Raney High School seems indicative of some doubt that Central and Hall Highs will be open. Dean Higgins' statement would seem to follow this same reasoning, and I was disturbed to have a high school teacher tell me Saturday that never since all this started has there been such a feeling of discouragement as right now. Constantly, even since the Federal Court rulings on Acts 4 and 5 and the statement of our School Board, mothers seek our advice, trying to weigh probabilities, worried to the point of discussing moving out of Arkansas in order to educate their children.

I do not know if silence and inactivity will be more effective than raising a voice in our efforts to preserve our public school system. I do fear that silence and inactivity may not serve to hold together the splendid organization the Women's Emergency Committee has built. But I again assure you we shall consider the full import of your thoughtful suggestion. Perhaps our committee has been using faulty methods. Your advice will help us reevaluate our program and we are grateful that you took the time and trouble to give us your observations.

I'll gladly report to you our decision, and sometime, at your convenience, I'd be pleased if we could talk together and so share our views and impressions more fully. I feel it is most important that we all work together for the future welfare of our children and our city.

Most sincerely

Vivion L. Brewer

The consensus of our executive board decision was a fervent "Let's carry on!"

In January, the AAUW (Little Rock branch) had reported on a survey of eighty-five Little Rock business men, reaching the conclusion that business at Little Rock had suffered because of the school crisis. The Governor had commented that this was not necessarily so. Anne Brown Helvenston, with an A.B. in history from Boston University, an M.A. in experimental psychology from the University of Arkansas and further work in the field of human development at the University of Chicago, pondered this and came up with the idea for a comprehensive survey of economic conditions in Little Rock. She had carefully detailed her plan and our executive committee was enthusiastic. This meant untold hours of very tiring work for hundreds of women, but again I was thrilled by the zeal, the talents and the endurance of our dedicated woman who labored long and without complaint during those hot summer months to compile the statistics and the comments necessary to the production of our LITTLE ROCK REPORT. In time, hundreds of copies of this report were to go to almost every state in our Union and to many foreign countries, at the request of the addressees.

Early in June, Forrest Rozell, Executive Secretary of the Arkansas Education Association, made a statement saying that the teachers were not disturbed. Many of the teachers to whom we talked gave us a decidedly contradictory impression.

For the use of our members we compiled a list of the questions parents most often asked us, and attached to it quotations from *Action Patterns in School Desegregation* (see Appendix 5).

Once more Velma Powell with thoughtful concern, developed a list of suggestions to be given to the School Board. Once more the executive committee carefully checked and rechecked each one. Dottie Morris and I took the final draft to Superintendent Powell, who appeared interested and receptive. On July 21 at our invitation, Mr. Tucker, Mr. Matson and Mr. Lamb came to Mrs. Terry's to listen to us patiently. We discussed disciplinary measures at length; we urged arrangement of teachers' meetings to prepare the teachers for the problems of integration; we suggested meetings with parents to answer their questions; we hoped they would meet with the Negro groups in a show of good faith. We gave each of them a copy of the ideas we had so painstakingly compiled (see Appendix 6). They thanked us politely and assured us they planned to operate the high schools. We were never sure that they read or appreciated our advice.

We sought advice and cooperation from a group of men we knew to be friendly: Ed Lester, Attorney; Victor Ray, Editor of a labor paper; Joe Hardin, former Vice President of the ArkLa Gas Company; Jimmy Harrison, labor; Maurice Mitchell, Attorney; Odell Smith, labor; Forrest Rozzell, Arkansas Education Association; Boyd Ridgeway, Chamber of Commerce; Lefty Hawkins, public relations; and Henry Woods, Attorney. All of these sat around Mrs. Terry's table with Mrs. Terry, Velma Powell, Dottie Morris, Anne Helvenston, Barbara Ashmore, Irene Samuel and myself. There was so much to talk about that I had more difficulty focusing the discussion than I'd ever had with our women's meetings. Finally, Odell Smith, who is an expert at handling a session, interrupted the flow of interesting but irrelevant tales to remind our guests sternly, "What she wants to know is how we can help them. Let's get down to business."

Should the men work with us, or should they form a separate committee? How do we contrive to get people to stand together? Where can we seek more funds? What safety measures could be taken? What if there is a special session of the legislature? Could we get help in organizing a strong state group? We compiled a list of measures which should be enforced to combat the threat of violence: municipal ordinances permitting the police to pick up potential agitators; specific direction of the city police by the city board of directors; building of morale of the police force by the Chamber of Commerce; information given to the FBI agents; contact made with federal Attorney General William R. Rogers; sermons against violence by ministers two weeks before school opening; a request by business men for statements from the City Manager and the Chief of Police; published pictures of maintenance crews painting and freshening the high schools for occupancy; meetings of parents with the principals of the high schools.

Our greatest concern now was for the *peaceful* opening of the schools. Since we were asked by many mothers and teachers what we believed about the probabilities of open schools, we realized there must be many people asking the same questions among themselves. I spent many hours at my desk trying to instill in worried women a more serene confidence than I felt myself, both for the assured opening of the schools and the faith that there could be no violence this time. Since no one else had spoken out, on the day we met with the men I've named above, the WEC issued a statement to the two newspapers:

> The Women's Emergency Committee — now 1572 strong — wishes to make this statement for the reassurance of our community and particularly of the parents: We have the utmost confidence that Little Rock is a law abiding city and that adequate protection for the peaceful opening of our schools will be provided.

Perhaps as a result of this meeting and this statement, on July 15, abut one-hundred citizens met in the Marquee Room at the Lafayette Hotel and a number of business and professional men organized a Committee for the Peaceful Operation of Public Schools. This gave our ink-stained office force another job. Mr. Gaston Williamson, an attorney, as chairman of this group, wrote a lengthy statement which was mimeographed and mailed out by the WEC.

On July 12, Sunday, at 2 p.m., Labor's Committee to Preserve Free Public Schools held a meeting in the auditorium of the Arkansas Education Association building. Mr. Odell Smith had asked me to make a short talk. I recall that Ted Lamb also spoke. But the meeting itself was what made that hot trip into town well worth while. Mr. Smith was a chairman *non-pareil.* Despite noticeable opposition, he maneuvered the discussion and the voting as a magician pulls a rabbit out of a hat, and before I could follow or apprehend his methods, he had triumphantly secured the passage of a resolution to maintain the public schools. I was amused, amazed and admiring. I can't say I admired my resultant publicity but it also amused and amazed me. The Capital Citizens Council Newsletter No. 3, under date of July 28, 1959, included the following:

> ... Odell Smith, Victor Ray and (of all people) Mrs. Joe Brewer stacked the meeting and went into the now familiar song and dance routine to the tune of "We favor Public Education (Mixed, of course.)" We do not know Mr. Smith, Mr. Ray nor Mrs. Brewer personally, nor do we care to. However, we do know many, many card carrying members of organized labor and to the man, they are dead set against Negroized white schools...

The Little Rock School Board announced it would open the high schools under the pupil placement law. The majority of its members felt this was the key to the school problems. Everett Tucker and Superintendent Powell appeared happy to have their pictures in the local papers as they flew to Charlotte, North Carolina, where the pupil assignment plan had resulted in little integration. They came home prepared to implement the plan with equal success. The *Arkansas Gazette* detailed this plan on June 28, report by Bill Lewis:

> Arkansas' two almost-identical pupil assignment laws, in the opinion of one attorney well-versed in their provisions, are designed to permit voluntary segregation without permitting discrimination....

1. They do not lend themselves to use as the basis for "class" suits but can result in suits involving only individuals or limited numbers, and

2. They set up a number of administrative hurdles that must be passed before integration suits reach the courts, each of them intended to further reduce the number of plaintiffs who ultimately run the administrative gamut without falling.

... the following factors to be considered in assignment, transfer or continuance of pupils in the schools or within classrooms "or other facilities thereof."

1. Available room and teaching capacity in the various schools.

2. Availability of transportation facilities.

3. The effect of the admission of new pupils upon established or proposed academic programs.

4. The suitability of established curricula for particular pupils.

5. The adequacy of the pupil's academic preparation for admission to a particular school and curriculum.

6. The scholastic aptitude and relative intelligence or mental energy or ability of the pupil.

7. The psychological qualification of the pupil for the type of teaching and associations involved.

8. The effect of admission of the pupil upon the academic progress of other students in a particular school or facility thereof.

9. The effect of admission of the pupil upon the prevailing academic standards at a particular school.

10. The psychological effect upon the pupil of attendance at a particular school.

11. The possibility of breaches of the peace or ill will or economic retaliation within the community.

12. The home environment of the pupil.

13. The maintenance or severance of established social and psychological relationships with other pupils and with teachers.

14. The choice and interests of the pupil.

15. The morals, conduct, health and personal standards of the pupil, and

16. The request or consent of parents of guardians and the reasons assigned therefor.

The WEC had been urging that the Board take positive steps to register pupils at the public high schools, since the parents and students were still unconvinced that the schools would indeed reopen, and many were considering making other plans for their coming school year. Also the WEC members

187

who lived in the Hall High district, the locale of the "Cadillac Brigade," suggested that the Hall High area be changed in order to include some Negroes and so refute the propaganda that Hall patrons wanted to integrate Central but would not tolerate Negroes in their own school.

On July 21, registration began at the four public high schools. Enrollment during the first three days stood at 1,632, compared with 3,665 who would have been eligible to enroll the previous year, Raney High School announced an enrollment of 1,235 students. Thirty Negroes enrolled for Central High School but only five Negroes had been assigned to Hall, three to Central. This, significantly, was three fewer than had attended Central in the 1957-58 session. Once more the NAACP entered an action in the courts, challenging the use of the placement law. Wiley A. Branton of Pine Bluff, Arkansas, an astute black attorney, asked that the right of Negro students to attend Central, Hall and Tech be limited only by the areas in which they lived. The School Board in earlier July had announced changes in Hall High's attendance area to include Negro students. They also asked Mr. Faubus for any plan that he might have to maintain segregation legally. On July 29, the governor suggested in a letter to Everett Tucker and other board members that Horace Mann, the all Negro high school, and Hall High, of the "Cadillac Brigade" area, be integrated leaving Central High for those preferring segregation, a plan which obviously would not comply with the federal mandate.

The Capital Citizens Council announced that it would take action "and not in the courts" to prevent any more school integration at Little Rock. This did not serve to alleviate the fears of the parents for the safety of their children if the schools did open. The WEC asked the City Manager and the City Directors to make a strong statement. Mayor Werner C. Knoop finally made their stand clear:

> The City Manager Board has not changed its previously announced policy. That policy is that it will not tolerate violence but that it will not take direct steps to enforce the integration order of the Federal Court. If and when Central High School is integrated, the responsibility for enforcement is clearly that of the federal government. The municipal government of Little Rock will not assist in integrating the school. However, we will protect life and property in the city.

Governor Faubus repeated that there would be violence, so much that the federal government would have to use force again, and "live ammunition" to carry out the Federal Court order for desegregation.

We renewed our pleas to the city directors for a reassuring statement. At length, City Manager Dean I. Dauley released a new policy statement by the City Board of Directors: "Knowing that this is a law abiding community and conscious of their responsibility to the citizens of Little Rock, the Board of Directors has instructed the Police Department to deal firmly and quickly in the protection of life and property should the need arise."

The School Board announced unequivocally that

it *would* "open our schools." Facing the inevitable renewed attack of "integrationists," I felt it necessary that the WEC make an affirming statement. En route home from the office, I composed it, and from a public telephone booth, called Bill Lewis of the *Gazette* staff to read it to him:

> Since the aim of our Committee is to reopen our four closed high schools in accordance with law and order, we approve every definite move toward this goal. All the world is watching us and we feel the announcement of the School Board today will be accepted as one step toward reclaiming the once proud reputation of Little Rock. May I reiterate: we are convinced that nothing could be more important to the future of Little Rock than the peaceful opening and operation of our public schools as will be shown very compellingly by the results of a broad survey of industry and skilled personnel which the WEC is now completing and which will be available to the public in the next week or two.

The WEC sent out a summertime news letter, its second letter to the membership, under date of July 30. By now we had learned to date our materials, one of our earlier omissions. Maybe we were always too rushed to think of the date. Maybe we refused to face the longevity of the WEC. The headline of this particular letter was joyous:

LITTLE ROCK'S HIGH SCHOOLS
TO BE OPEN IN SEPTEMBER!

We told of writing a number of legislators and over 400 people over the state, asking them to contact their legislators with a request that they oppose any interference in the Little Rock school situation. We were still worried about the possibility of a special session. We spoke of our various surveys and thanked all of those who had given so many hours to these and other projects during the hot, harried summer. We proudly told of Mrs. Eleanor Roosevelt's story of the WEC in her syndicated column, of the complimentary notice given the WEC in an article by Mr. Nat Griswold in the *New South,* and the splendid coverage of the activities of the WEC in the June issue of the YWCA magazine. Sadly we announced that Mrs. J.O. Powell, a member of our executive committee and "one of our first members," had moved to Corona, California. We ended with a sentence in bold type: **Be sure to pay your poll tax.**

Emotional tensions had become almost all Joe and I could bear this year, and I knew that we must have a respite. Brutal, almost unbearable personal harassment had followed Joe's demotion. He was deprived of his aides and his secretary. He was allowed no specified parking space. He was isolated in an office and denied any free time. No longer was he permitted to leave the building to attend his Rotary Club, and his lunch hour was staggered to coincide with that of none of his former staff and friends. A daily written report of his activities, minute by minute, was demanded. Sadistic accusations broke his spirit. Yet I begged him to hold on. I still believed this must be a horrible nightmare, that one day truth would conquer and justice prevail. Fighting desperately for Joe, I had written the President of the United States, Dwight D. Eisenhower; I wrote the Honorable Sumner G. Whittier, Administrator of the Veterans Administration. I had contacted Brooks Hays and a friend in the Justice Department. I had written Senator Fulbright. Mrs. Terry had written a close friend of Sumner Whittier's. Harry Ashmore had written the Attorney General, William P. Rogers. Long hours of worry, careful composition and typing had changed nothing. Polite, sometimes lengthy answers explained nothing and brought no relief. I began to believe that Orval E. Faubus controlled the federal government as well as Arkansas.

Very few in the WEC knew of our ordeal, but I had forewarned the executive committee that I planned a leave of absence and asked if everyone wanted a vacation for a short time. Fortunately, although no open meetings were scheduled, the executive committee voted to continue its weekly sessions and to keep the office open and functioning. There was much yet to do to complete our major survey for the *Little Rock Report.*

We thought we were escaping at a time the WEC could do little more toward the opening of the schools, and believed we would be home again well ahead of the re-opening in September. So we happily packed a fried chicken supper and secluded ourselves in a bedroom in Car 83 of the Missouri

Pacific train to Chicago at 3:45 Sunday afternoon, August 2. It was intriguing that our porter, Mr. P. James Johnson of Little Rock, not only recognized us and knew our name but knew where we lived. He asked if he might come fishing in "our lake" and we have been glad to welcome him many times in the years since.

My going away present was the feature article in the *Gazette* that Sunday. The article reported WEC member Grace (Mrs. Robert) Malakoff's preliminary statement on Anne Helvenston's survey plan.

I wrote her a grateful letter for this propitious bon voyage, and we did have a beautiful, relaxing trip across southern Canada and down the coast of Washington, Oregon and California, but in San Francisco, I glimpsed a sensational headline which made my stomach turn over: "All Little Rock riots." We swerved our car around the block but could not find the paper boy nor any similar paper. Was I having hallucinations? I sought a telephone and called Mrs. Terry. She reassured me that the report was much exaggerated, but imagine the glorious shock of this: *The schools were open!*

This was August 12, 1959, and the days between August 2 and August 12 had been frantic ones for everyone connected with the school situation. Gradually, I learned the details.

Some of the members of the School Board had composed an absurd letter to the Governor, a letter at the center of a comedy that so narrowly escaped being a tragedy. It read:

Governor Orval E. Faubus
State Capitol
Little Rock, Arkansas

Dear Governor Faubus:

Sometime back you suggested through the press that you might have a workable plan for the operation of our Little Rock school system. Our Board then replied through the press that we would like for you to present your plan. We meant no offense in speaking through the newspapers rather than directly to you. This has become so much the procedure these past two years that we may have taken for granted that the press was the accepted medium of communication.

If you agree, we would prefer that any matter we take up regarding your high office, that we deal directly with you. You in turn, if the matter deals with the Little Rock school system, would make your first contacts with us. We would be genuinely appreciative of this procedure on both our parts.

We have carefully read and studied your suggested plan as submitted to us. We truly hope you were not serious in some of your suggestions. We cannot believe that you prefer (1200?) white students being integrated with 1000 (?) of our negro students (use correct figures) of Hall High and Horace Mann High Enrollment. We only had 9 Negro students with 2,000 white students at the time you closed the high schools.

We would not argue with you regarding what is and what is not the law of the land. We are simply trying, in our limited way, to open our public schools. We are trying hard to represent every parent in Little Rock by using your own good placement laws and permitting the smallest degree of integration and still maintain our public school system.

In your letter you place much emphasis upon our own state laws and our state constitution. You emphasize to us that the Supreme Court might be ignored. It has been our observation that even you, when directly ordered to abandon the use of our state laws, have done so. History records many debates and protests on rulings of the courts, but eventually we have always returned to orderly obedience or an orderly correction.

You do express one fact that we would like to accept and encourage wholeheartedly. We fervently hope that you accept and use it as your guide in dealing with us. As expressed in the last paragraph of the third page of your letter dated July 28, you state: "Even so, it has been clearly demonstrated that the people of Arkansas will accept the freedom of choice, on a community basis, of either segregated or integrated schools. This is simply evidenced by the non-interference with the operation of integrated schools at Charleston, Fayetteville, and other places in our state."

We believe Little Rock has now made a free choice. By their majority vote they have chosen members of the School Board who publicly committed themselves to maintain our public schools even with some degree of integration. With Raney High School having both yours and our support we believe Little Rock has a freer choice than most cities. We shall be glad to join with an orderliness that will reflect credit upon the state, upon you, and upon the city of Little Rock.

As a demonstration of our desire to cooperate with you and as a demonstration of our desire to represent all of the tax-paying parents of Little Rock, who want a school wholly segregated, we would be willing to discuss with you and the board of Raney High School, the possibility of our leasing and operating Raney High School as a part of our Little Rock public school system with no tuition to parents.

We would use Raney High's own teaching staff, their own curriculum, and carry on their program to the best of our ability.

With the students and parents of Raney High being strongly opposed to any degree of segregation, with Central and Hall High being available for Negro applicants, we do not believe there would be any Negroes to apply for admission to Raney High. Should they do so, we believe that with the use of the placement program and without violating the spirit of the court orders we could transfer the applicants to either of the other schools. Should all of these efforts on our part fail and the court order integration of Raney High School, then in keeping with our conception of a lease provision, we would immediately return it to the private Raney board.

You have suggested that we use Central High on this basis as the free choice of a segregated school. We have already been ordered by the courts to integrate this school. Unlike Raney High School, its physical plant is public property and could not

> be turned over to a private board to continue its operation on a segregated basis, as we could Raney High if ordered to integrate by the courts.
>
> If this could be worked out, and we would give you our whole hearted cooperation in an attempt to do it, we feel we would have solved every problem in keeping with your expressed wishes.
>
> Your cooperation is sincerely sought.
>
> Yours very truly,

On August 4, the School Board met at 8:30 a.m. and voted five to one (Ted Lamb) to send this letter to Mr. Faubus. Cottrell decided to deliver it personally and left the meeting to go directly to the state Capitol. As the other members straggled out, they met Bobbie Forster, the able *Democrat* reporter, who told them that Dr. Raney had just announced the abandonment of Raney High School. The four members dashed to their cars to pursue Cottrell in order to reclaim the letter. With good luck they overtook him in the press room of the governor's office, just on the brink of disaster. As Lefty Hawkins remarked, "it was a Marx Brothers comedy," and it *was* funny but it could have been betrayal leading to ruin. We took another look at the School Board.

Although Raney High had added rooms to its building in July, on that August 4th, as Bobbie Forster told the School Board members, T.J. Raney withdrew the school's funds from the bank and announced that Raney High School would not open, due to lack of money. The next day the Little Rock

School Board announced that the public high schools would open earlier than scheduled, on August 12. This change of plans was an ingenuous idea of Ted Lamb's for circumventing Governor Faubus' calling a special session of the legislature, and possible further legislation which might keep the schools closed.

Dr. Malcolm G. Taylor, president of the Capital Citizens Council, tried to panic parents with, "It seems our schools are in the hands of reckless daredevils who are willing to open the schools in the height of a polio epidemic in order to force integration."

Dr. Mason G. Lawson, City Health Officer, threw cold water on the scare by saying that most of the reported polio cases involved children under ten, far below high school age.

Governor Faubus was ready as usual with an inflammatory statement: "They (the Little Rock School Board) put off the opening of the schools before to try to get the Negroes in. Now they are moving *up* the opening date to get the Negroes in. (In 1958 the decision to delay the opening of the public high schools for two weeks, was made awaiting the ruling of the U.S. Supreme Court on whether the School Board had to integrate the schools. Not one of the Board members who made that decision in 1958 was on the board in the fall of 1959.)

Ted Lamb had the inspiration to telephone Dr. Jonas Salk who issued a public statement that there would be no increased danger of polio due to the opening of the high schools. This helped to quiet the rumors, but our Governor was undaunted. On August 11, the eve of the school re-opening, having announced his plan only a little more than an hour before he went on, Governor Faubus again spoke from the TV screen. He quoted frequently from his TV speech of May 22 in an "I told you so" vein and he attacked members of the School Board, Tucker, Lamb and Matson, the Chief of Police Eugene G. Smith, Harry Ashmore, and the NAACP. "If local authorities, school boards and police would not relieve federal authorities of the unpleasant task of forcing integration, then the federals would soon withdraw and let the people run their own affairs." Mr. Faubus emphasized that he was not throwing in the sponge. "If token integration is effected, there are many ways in which you who are opposed can still resist. The struggle is not by any means ended. Regardless of the outcome tomorrow you must resolve to continue the struggle for freedom." Chatting with reporters after his speech, he said he didn't plan to see anyone the next day. These were his plans "at present time." He added, "It's been quieter but at the same time there has been a bit more bitterness in Little Rock. Clashes and disorder would just add to it." Asked if he had any concrete reports of trouble in connection with the school opening, the governor replied, "Yes, I do." He declined to elaborate.

Everyone: WEC, parents, sympathizers, feared renewed violence. Many hoped for the involvement of the U.S. Marshalls, but the School Board and the City Directors made no move to ask for them. Our staff checked each of the Little Rock police and found

23 had signed our enemy CROSS petitions, only six had signed the STOP petitions. Twenty-six lived outside the district. Two were members of the white Citizens Council. These statistics were not reassuring and August 12th found the city jittery.

Hall High School opened that morning with not one incident, with three Negro girls attending. But there was an attempt to cause trouble at Central High, as Governor Faubus had prophesied. Janet Johnston described it in her written report:

> A crowd formed at the Capitol around ten o'clock, calling for Governor Faubus. The Governor spoke to them, saying that he didn't think violence would do much good. Mrs. Dale Alford also spoke to the crowd. (At Orlando, Florida, Representative Dale Alford had orated that school integration was "merely the Trojan horse by which the enemy will attempt to destroy America." He identified the "enemy" as socialism and said it was creeping not only into the government but also into the schools and churches. "The Supreme Court decision is not the law of the land. Our public schools are being destroyed before our very eyes by the Warren dominated Supreme Court. The people are sovereign; not nine men.") The crowd was addressed by several other less well-known speakers. City police arrested boys who had some tear gas bombs in their possession. Since they were on state property, they were turned over to state police, who released them. The crowd of about 200 left the Capitol grounds and marched to Central High School, carrying

American flags in the front row and bouncing placards reading: "Governor Faubus. Save our Christian America." They were asked by police to stop a block away from Central, but proceeded to try to go through police lines. The police then turned fire hoses on them, which broke up the march. Central High opened peacefully, without further incident, with two Negroes in attendance.

On the second day there was only one Negro in the school, for Elizabeth Eckford had discovered that she already had accumulated enough credits to receive her diploma and had withdrawn. Police had stayed on the job but all was quiet on August 13 both at Central and at Hall. Only some six spectators watched silently.

Janet Johnston wrote that Faubus castigated the School Board and the police. The Capital Citizens Council accused the City police of brutality, as did Mrs. Dale Alford, who demanded action. Two women filed a $50,000 damage suit against Police Chief Eugene G. Smith in Federal District Court, charging their civil rights were violated in incidents occurring near Central High on opening day. However, the City Board of Directors backed the police action, and City Manager Dean I. Dauley said there were movies available that covered everything that happened at the Central High School demonstration. Obscene phone calls burgeoned once more, but both the City Board and the police were commended by hundreds of responsible citizens. The WEC moved into a familiar pattern with congratulatory letters to the Chief of Police, to the City Directors, to the members of the School Board.

During these suspenseful days, I had many long distance telephone conversations with both Mrs. Terry and Mrs. Samuel. I was fortunate to have immediate and detailed information, for in Los Angeles I had an unsolicited entrepreneur. Lew Irwin, KABC TV network and KPOL radio, asked me for an interview, and brought his equipment to my niece's garden in Pasadena to tape it. I found it easy and pleasant to talk with such a sympathetic, friendly person and though I never did hear the tape, and was unable to secure a copy of it for the WEC files, I was told it went well. Irv Fang, of the *Pasadena Star News*, who was to win a Neiman Fellowship, wrote a strong editorial for the WEC. Paul V. Coates, whose half hour TV interviews in the style of Mike Wallace were popular on the west coast and were syndicated in a number of major cities in the United States, sent his staff writer, Mike Sommers, to interview me. On Thursday evening, we drove to the KTTV TV station at Sunset and Van Ness Boulevards in Hollywood so I might make a tape for him. Joe, my niece and her husband, Patricia and Skipper Rostker, and Velma and Jay Powell who had driven in from Corona, went with me. They arranged themselves along the wall of the studio facing me, but when Mr. Coates entered, he insisted that they retire to the monitoring room adjacent. This was my first experience in a large studio, and I was so intrigued by all the activity that

I forgot to be nervous — somewhat tense, yes, for I was not sure of all I might be asked and I was extremely eager to say nothing which might in any way inflame the situation at home or injure the program of the WEC. While a number of huge spotlights bore down on me from several angles, I watched aides perfecting Mr. Coates' make-up, his hair, the set of his tie and lapels, and I wished somebody would be so kind to me. But I soon forgot that as we began to talk, and I found myself enjoying that strange half hour.

When I had first arrived at the studio, I had asked when the program might be shown, thinking I might alert a few friends, but I was told that this depended on their schedules and so the showing was quite indefinite. I know now that it in fact depended entirely on me. As I left following the interview, Mr. Sommers told me I would be on that very night at ten-thirty and again the following afternoon at two. Listening that night, I felt I had said quite a lot, but in the light of developments since, the tape of this interview which was made by a friend in Connecticut, sounds so very cautious that I wonder how it was of much interest. I do not know how many times it was shown, but I was advised that it was televised in San Francisco as well as Los Angeles, New York, Philadelphia, St. Louis, Fort Worth and Dallas. Many kind letters, not a single negative one, came from strangers in these areas, and even some money, which made me regret that I had not made a real pitch for contributions.

Mr. Coates, who also wrote a column for the *Mirror News*, gave one of his days to the story of the

WEC, and later gave us permission to use this column or any part of it in our publicity. He did more than this for us, but that is another tale to be told in another chapter.

Joe and I flew home on August 22, and there I was to find that my trip to California was no secret. A friend obtained for me a copy of the first issue of the *States' Rights Digest*, on the front page of which was a large picture of Orval E. Faubus and under that a smaller one of me, a reprint of the photograph made by the reporter in Pasadena. The news item was headed: "Outsider Heads Integrationist Women's Group," and told of my interview in Los Angeles, adding, "Mrs. Brewer, who is not a resident of Little Rock and who has no children, is the wife of an ex-Air Force officer who is now employed by the V.A. Hospital. The Brewers live at Scott in Lonoke County. Mrs. Brewer spoke repeatedly of 'our children' and 'our schools.' She has no children in the Little Rock school district and any taxes she pays is to Lonoke County."

This issue of the *States Rights Digest* became a keep-sake, and I made every effort to obtain subsequent issues, but at no time did I or the WEC recognize it publicly. Instead, this manner of attack was a stimulus. If we were not succeeding, why would our enemies bother?

Eight

Bombs

Joe and I arrived home on a Saturday and I al located Sunday to settling in, but Monday morning I was back in the office and busy reviewing the survey. Much hard and expert work had been whipping it into shape. Anne Helvenston, the *Report's* creator, became Survey Director, and Grace Malakoff was the Survey Editor. It would be difficult to estimate which one contributed more to its success.

In June, Anne had brought the Executive Committee a carefully detailed survey proposal, with guidelines for discussion of advantages and disadvantages. By now, we were imbued with the go-ahead sprit and refused to be worried about the magnitude of the work involved. The WEC Board unanimously accepted the proposal. To get started on the right track, Anne Helvenston and Irene Samuel went to the Arkansas Industrial Research Center (A.I.R.C.)

to consult with friends whose wives were members of the WEC. These men were impressed with the plan and offered to help get the ball rolling. With their invaluable advice, the WEC mimeographed Survey Instructions, then carefully selected a number of attractive, energetic women (both attributes were important) to act as interviewers. On June 17, eighteen women (see Appendix 7) gathered in our office to listen to suggestions from Ralph Gray and Winston Beard of the A.I.R.C., and to receive a copy of the Survey Instructions and a check list for Survey Personnel.

Each interviewer also bore a letter of introduction signed by me as chairman of the WEC, and perhaps this accounted in part for the infinite variety of experiences the women reported. There was evidence that in some quarters, the WEC was not welcome. Sometimes they were bluntly refused admittance to a plant. In others, suspicious and nervous management resented women, however attractive, "prying." Among many lessons, we learned that we must use care in sending women with "Yankee accents" to offices staffed by southern men. The "outsider" was anathema in our community. Yet, in the majority of cases, our interviewers were welcomed politely and the answers we needed were given readily. Obviously, many officials were glad to talk about their serious problems.

As the data were assembled in our office from day to day, we knew this idea had been cogent. Groups of women, in growing numbers, began to spend days in our cramped quarters, or more often in one of their homes, tabulating the accumulated information. Grace and Anne began to summarize and edit. As copy was available, many women helped with mimeographing, but most of that exhausting and very dirty work was done by Jo Menkus (Mrs. David), Carroll Holcomb (Mrs. Norman) and Jenny Harrell (Mrs. J.A., Jr.) Effective illustrations for the book were drawn by Ellen Rae Kaufman.

All of this took months of dedicated labor. Once the statistics were determined, there were graphs to be made, text to be written, pictures to be included, the order to be determined, mimeographing to be completed, and finally the book of sixty-five pages of 8½" x 11" sheets to be assembled and stapled within blue covers. The last enclosure was a graphic editorial cartoon by Clifford H. "Baldy" Baldowski: "First We Closed Our Schools, Then One Thing Led to Another" in a dramatic 14" x 17" form which had to be folded meticulously in order to fit neatly in the book.

When at last the *Report* was ready for distribution, our Executive Committee argued about the wisdom of publicizing it. We were divided on this issue. The schools *were* open and some women felt the truth of our findings might antagonize some of the power structure toward our future program. I consulted Gene Fretz of the public relations firm of Hawkins and Fretz, probably because Lefty Hawkins had been helpfully cooperative during the reopening-of-the-schools days and because Gene Fretz was a friend from the time he married one of my niece's girlhood chums. Certainly their fee was inconsequential and their advice was accepted by our Board with full accord. The statement they prepared for us was released on Sunday, September 6, 1959:

FOR RELEASE: Sunday, September 6, 1959

LITTLE ROCK REPORT:
The City, Its People, Its Business

Statement from Mrs. Joe R. Brewer, Chairman of the Women's Emergency Committee to Open Our Schools:

This report is based on a survey of Little Rock industrial, management and professional people.

The original intent was to publish the report before the schools opened. We offer it to the public now with the belief it may be of help in other areas. The interviews started early in June when the school outlook was uncertain. All the work was done by members of the Women's Emergency Committee to Open Our Schools who volunteered their time and talents to this project.

All Arkansas communities which are interested in education are interested in the Little Rock story. This report shows that business and the people in Little Rock have suffered during the past two years. With our schools now reopened, there is a new day in our city. We feel that this report definitely indicates that the business factors which had been weakened will be restored as the school situation stabilizes and the business trends in Little Rock will push upward steadily.

Because it has historical value, and because we see in this report a constructive promise, copies have been sent to all of the members of the Arkansas General Assembly. Copies of the survey

---

are available at $1 a copy, from our office, P.O. Box 3244, Forest Heights Station.

With the release of the report, the Committee's Executive Board has voted to change the name of the organization to the Women's Emergency Committee for Public Schools. Our first goal has been achieved by the community — the schools ARE open. But we will continue a positive program in support of public education — to preserve public education and to encourage improvement of the schools.

There can be no surprise that the first run of the *Little Rock Report: The City, Its People, Its Business 1957-1959* had some imperfections in it. We struggled to insert hand-written corrections and for the most part this first edition was absorbed by our own members and friends. News of it had spread, however, and orders began to pour in from over the United States and even from foreign countries. Over some objection, I insisted on holding these orders until we completed a correction edition. I felt very strongly that libraries must not shelve WEC material which was in error. So we hurried with a second edition — and a third. Jo Menkus was never given appropriate recognition for her patient devotion to the grimy, tedious job of mimeographing.

We sent complimentary copies of the *Report* to many public figures, the City Board of Directors, our state legislators, our representatives in the U.S. Congress, and to the Little Rock School Board. We explained that we had planned to publish this information prior to the opening of school and we added:

> We are happy and grateful that the high
> schools are now open. With this new day
> we have every confidence that business
> trends in Little Rock are responding favor-
> ably and will surge upward steadily. It is
> solely with the belief that it may help in
> other communities that we make the sur-
> vey public at this time. We hope that you
> will think the report has this constructive
> value and historical merit.

More orders came with every mail. We had hoped
to issue the entire production of the *Report* gratis,
but the demand so exceeded our expectation that
we felt constrained to charge $1.00 per copy to cover
our expenses of reproduction and the mailing costs.
All of the labor continued to be volunteer.

The Southern Regional Council in Atlanta, Georgia, asked permission to brief the *Report* and we
readily, gratefully gave our consent. They published
their *Report No. L11* as of October 12, 1959, and it
was distributed widely.

Indubitably, although the peaceful opening of
the high schools was the reward for all of our work,
the *Little Rock Report* was the outstanding production of the WEC. Years later, I met people from distant states who knew about the *Report* but were very
vague about the history of the WEC — or, indeed,
the details of the school closing.

All of us in the WEC felt the *Report* was *great*,
yet deplored the obvious fact that it proved that it is
the pocketbook which speaks. "Let us be glad something speaks," we told ourselves, for time proved that

Little Rock had learned one lesson and perhaps our *Report* had been the text book. We clung to the hope that the lesson would not be forgotten and that our dark days would further the determination of other cities not to emulate "Little Rock."

Ten days after the public high schools opened, the Little Rock School Board laid its entire program for dealing with the integration crises before Federal Judge E. Miller of Fort Smith, Arkansas, for his approval. They asked specifically that he:

1. approve the "good faith compliance" of the School Board with the court orders governing the desegregation of the schools.

2. approve the assignment procedures adopted and being followed by the School Board and Superintendent Terrell E. Powell. (Under these procedures the number of Negro students who applied to attend previously all white high schools had been trimmed from 60 to 6.)

3. approve the Board's "non-discriminatory operation of the schools."

4. approve "all other affirmative steps" taken by the Board members "in the performance of their official duties."

Six days later, on August 28, 1959, about 8:20 in the evening, two unidentified men tossed two tear gas bombs into the foyer of the offices of the Board of Education. Five members of the School Board, meeting in a room on the second floor, filed down a back stairway into the street and within thirty minutes had resumed their meeting in the boardroom of the Chamber of Commerce. Little damage had been done except to the nervous systems of our already up-tight citizens.

Because of the late summer heat, high school classes had been in session only on a half day basis, but they were to resume full schedule on September 8th, the date on which the elementary and junior high schools were to open their regular fall term. This would indicate that the eve of this date had been chosen with malice aforethought by the five men who were later convicted of the bombings which shook all of Little Rock to the core. Indeed, court testimony later revealed that initial plans for these bombings had been made as early as July, and had the high schools NOT opened in August, it is unlikely that any of the schools would have opened as scheduled.

September 7 was Labor Day. That night, within 38 minutes between 10:20 and 10:58, three bombs exploded in widely separated areas in rapid-fire succession. The first bomb demolished Fire Chief Nalley's city-owned station wagon which was parked in front of his rural home on Baseline Road. The family, asleep at the time, was unharmed. Mr. Nalley later hazarded a guess that he was chosen for attack because a fire hose had been used to help police quell the demonstration at Central High School on August 12.

The second bomb hit the School Board building, badly damaging two rooms and blowing out the windows of the Carmelite Home next door where Catholic nuns were asleep. Mercifully no one was hurt.

The third bomb inflicted the greatest damage as it struck the Baldwin Company some nine blocks from the education offices. This was a construction company of which Mayor Werner Knoop was an executive with offices on the second floor. A steel panel was knocked into the street. The wall of an insurance company office next door was torn out. Windows in the Second Presbyterian Church across the street were blown out. The entire city had a bad case of jitters. Governor Faubus mourned that there were no limits to which his enemies would go to discredit him, and Attorney General Bruce Bennett attributed the bombings to the Communists. Everett Tucker said, "I don't know what anyone would expect to accomplish unless they are trying to put 22,000 children on the streets." The police, with the co-operation of the FBI, swarmed out to patrol, guard, check and investigate, and despite the agitation pervading Little Rock, the junior high and elementary schools opened on schedule.

Within seventy-two hours, three men had been taken into custody. A fourth was quickly apprehended and a fifth was later arrested. One of these, so the prosecutor said, had been a member of the Ku Klux Klan. The apparent leader, E.A. Lauderdale, long active in the Capital Citizens Council, had been defeated twice in elections for the city manager board (once in a close race with the then Mayor Werner C. Knoop); and his son was a fireman under Mr. Nalley's supervision. Amis Guthridge, attorney and spokesman for the Capital Citizens Council, represented both Lauderdale, a lumber dealer, and J.D. Sims, a truck driver. It all tied in.

The trials suffered some delays, which only served to heighten the nervous strain for all citizens, business men and parents most of all. Ultimately all five were convicted, but only one (the fall guy as we saw it) was sent off to prison within any reasonable time, and none served much of his sentence. A resume of the terms of the sentences and the time served, as reported in 1961, is of interest, especially when compared with the relatively more harsh sentences allotted to sit-inners in 1960:

Convict	Fine	Term	Served
Lauderdale	$500	3 years	5 mo. 11 days
Perry	0	3 years	5 mo. 8 days
Coggins	0	3 years	5 mo. 8 days
Sims*	0	5 years	1 yr., 9 mo., 20 days
Beavers	$500	5 years	sentence suspended

And we were not through with the terrorism. The year 1960 brought us two more cataclysmic incidents of bombing: one in February, one in July. Nor had the governor subsided. Although he said this fall of 1959, "Under the present circumstances, I don't think I would close the schools," (and we wondered if Senator Fulbright's long delayed and now

---

* Sims was the first one sentenced.

limited comment on the Little Rock situation on August 24: "Faubus erred in the school crisis" had any influence on this change of mind? — or had our *Little Rock Report?*) he could not let it go at that. "Whether the people like it or not, they're apparently reconciled to police state rule of federal authorities and the local police department." And Faubus appealed to the U. S. Supreme Court for a review of the decisions on the constitutionality of Acts 4 and 5.

Not one of us in the WEC felt our job was finished. On September 9, our Executive Committee met to consider our future and decided to hold an anniversary tea on September 16.

There was a wonderful bit of publicity on the eve of this anniversary. In the magazine section of the Sunday, September 13 edition of the *New York Times*, an article by Miss Gertrude Samuels, who had visited Little Rock and Pine Bluff at the time of the school re-opening, told of the work of the WEC. The article included a lovely picture of Mrs. Terry entitled "First Lady of Little Rock."

In addition to the enthusiastic acceptance of our altered name, policy and purpose, the business part of this meeting included a sign of changing times — or our reinforced courage. We announced that our telephone number was now listed, that we had a new and publicized post office box number at a branch near our office, and that we would continue regular open meetings the first Tuesday of each month at 1 p.m. at 411 East Seventh Street. Barbara Long had chaired a nominating committee, making a special effort to find a second vice chairman, an office heretofore unfilled, and to replace our recording secretary who had tendered her resignation. Barbara presented a slate which was adopted without hesitation and our fourth newsletter, in vivid yellow, dated September 30, 1959, listed the names of the officers and the members of the board:

Mrs. Joe R. Brewer, Chairman

Mrs. D.D. Terry, Vice-chairman

Mrs. Byron House, Jr., 2nd Vice-chairman

Mrs. John M. Samuel, Executive Secretary

Mrs. H. Charles Johnson, Recording Secretary

Miss Ada May Smith, Treasurer

Miss Parma Basham, Finance Committee

Mrs. Earl D. Cotton, Program Committee

Mrs. Heber Helvenston, Research and Statistics Committee

Mrs. Payton Kolb, Contacts with other organizations

Mrs. W.C. Johnson, Publicity Committee

Mrs. Robert Shults, Membership Committee

Mrs. W.H. Thompson and

Mrs. E. Grainger Williams, Policy Committee

Alternate board members included Mrs. Norman Holcomb, Mrs. David Menkus, Mrs. Frank N. Gordon, Mrs. Charles N. Henry and Mrs. Robert Malakoff.

This was further indication of our increasing bravery in wishing to publicize names because our newsletters invariably found their way into the hands of the press. This particular issue boxed in an important notice:

MARK YOUR CALENDAR NOW!

Next meeting — Tuesday, October 6, 1959, 1:00 p.m. Hear outstanding attorney on constitutional law. Mr. A.F. House will discuss General Assembly Joint Resolution No. 5, a proposed constitutional amendment which will affect our public schools. Place: 411 East 7th St.

This October sixth meeting was memorable and not because it fell on my birthday. Mr. House brought us our first public discussion of the proposed constitutional amendment No. 52, which was to be the center of our intensive work in 1960. I was disappointed that, perhaps due to his involvement in cases concerning the School Board which resigned in the fall of 1958, Mr. House refused publicity on his talk. I had no forewarning of his feeling about this so I could not alert the press to his desire to speak off the record. After the meeting had started, both Mr. House and I saw Roy Reed of the *Arkansas Gazette* coming up the long walk through the garden. Quickly Archie House said he did not want his talk to be publicized so I excused myself to stop Mr. Reed at the steps of the portico of the Terry Mansion. Mr. Reed's reaction was even more negative than mine, but I sympathized with his acrid exclamation, "When will people speak out?"

Our most urgent objective this fall of 1959 was the School Board election and we faced several dilemmas. Were we to fight for two or three places on the Board? Were appointed members to serve completed terms or only until the next election? Would the members appointed after the STOP election all decide to run? And when *was* the next election to be? The title of Act 248 of 1959 specified one date, the body of the act another. Under the circumstances, there was nothing to do but keep our files in readiness and bide our time, although we had long discussions of probabilities and possibilities. Alice Glover, President of the Little Rock Classroom Teachers Association came to our rescue. She filed suit to clarify this 1959 act, and on September 17th, Pulaski County Chancellor Murray O. Reed issued this ruling:

> 1. Since the new act makes no provision for how long an appointed member shall serve on a school board, a provision in Act 30 of 1935 still applies in that it specifies that an appointed member shall serve only until the next school election, rather than completing the unexpired term if it extends beyond the election.
>
> 2. The proper date of the school election is the first Tuesday of December, not the last Saturday in September.

The second part of the ruling was a relief but the first was something else. In effect, it gave the segregationist forces another chance to regain control of the Little Rock School Board. The case was appealed and our anxiety was lessened by one-third when the Supreme Court ruled that the terms of only two — not three — of the six men on the Little Rock School Board expired this year. In our September 30th letter we urged:

VOTE

VOLUNTEERS NEEDED call MO 4-1607 for committee assignments.

NEED FOR ACTION! ! Beginning soon, many of you will be called for jobs in connection with the school board election. Keep this in mind and save time to help when you are called. It was through your hard work that we are where we are.

PLEASE PREPARE FOR ACTION!

We knew we faced another emergency. Everett Tucker and Frank Mackey were opposed by Mothers' League candidates Margaret Morrison and Mrs. H.H. Ray. Despite our disenchantment with Everett Tucker, we could not afford to lose him or Frank Mackey to two outspoken segregationists. This meant untold hours of concentrated, tiring, and often boring work setting up card files on the qualified voters, verifying their addresses and checking the STOP and CROSS petitions to discover their probable vote.

Daily, volunteers crowded our small office to mark the cards and poll books. We used every inch of space available in the two small rooms. Sometimes there was a buzz of excitement as an unsuspected enemy was discovered. Sometimes there were tears when that unsuspected foe was a relative or a friend. But on the whole, silent, serious concentration focused on this monumental task.

There was one prelude to the election which was known to few. Late in September, a rumor reached Mrs. Terry that a Negro group planned to run one of its members for the School Board OR elect a segregationist Board to assure the closing of the schools in order to educate the public. We had been more and more concerned that some type of interracial committee must be organized, and better communication lines kept open between the WEC and the Negro community.

On the 29th of September, four Negroes attended the School Board meeting and were resoundingly rebuffed by its President, Everett Tucker. Reverend James T. McCullum, pastor of the Steele Memorial Baptist Church, as spokesman for the four, told the School Board of the need for an interracial committee and asked for one "representative each from your group and our group and a liaison agent from the administrative level."

Mr. Tucker's answer was a snub: "We are not aware of any lack of communication with the colored community and we are not maintaining communications with any one group more than we are with another." Rumors drifted in that the Negro community now believed that the WEC was against it. Perhaps this was due to our support of Everett Tucker. Perhaps our policy not to accept Negro members was at fault. We discussed this in our Executive Committee but we remained convinced that the WEC as a biracial organization could have no hope of influencing results of elections in favor of integrated schools.

Through friendly sources, we learned that a prominent young Negro physician had been selected to run for the School Board. Adolphine Terry and I were fearful for the effect of this on the city already in an exacerbated emotional atmosphere. "He'll be killed," Adolphine grieved. "We must talk with him." So she invited Dr. M.A. Jackson, Irene Samuel and myself for lunch in the den of her home.

Dr. Jackson was a tall, handsome man with fine features and an unidentifiable accent which he taught himself. He had worked as a barkeep at a country club to put himself through the University of Arkansas Medical School and had established a large practice in Little Rock. His manner was marked by a courteous dignity and our conversation was easy and pleasant. We told him of our grave concern for his own safety and for the future peace of our city. He accepted this, we thought, in good spirit, but he expressed his obligation to his friends who were backing him. Could we meet with them, he wondered? Our response was instant. Home at 5:19 p.m., I doubled back almost immediately to pick up Mrs. Terry at six. Together we drove to the home of Dr. Garman P. Freeman, where he and his wife, Dr. Jackson and five of their friends awaited us. Dr. Jackson was by far the most cordial of the group. The others were silent, almost grim, and why not? We had come to thwart their plans, to dim their hopes. *We* were the enemy.

221

As spokesman, I tried to explain our position gently and tactfully. I told of the persistent harassment all of us had suffered and prophesied that it would be a hundred fold worse for Dr. Jackson and his family. "Is your wife one to be distressed by obscene phone calls? You may be able to bear the nervous strain but is she? And what about your children? What if they are threatened?" I was sincerely worried, for him and for the danger of increased hate and prejudice. I tried to convince them that Mrs. Terry and I came as concerned individuals, not as representatives of the WEC, but I also assured them of the true friendship of the WEC and of our sympathy for their cause. "I can not, of course, pledge a future action for our Committee, but for myself, Dr. Jackson, I promise you that if in another year you want to run for any office in this city, I will do my utmost to support you."

(This I did, in a lone hold-out vote against the rest of the Executive Committee of the WEC in 1962, when Irene Samuel, still the executive secretary, and Pat House, then the chairman, log-rolled through the committee a vote to support Dr. J.A. Harrell, Jr. against Dr. Jackson. I had no feud with Dr. Harrell, as I explained to him personally when he came to see me at my sister-in-law's home, and to a group of men and women planning to promote Dr. Harrell's candidacy. In fact, I did not know him although I had known and liked his wife as she volunteered in our office. But I had made a promise to Dr. Jackson and I intended to keep it to the best of my ability. Word of this split in the WEC reached Bobbie Forster of the *Arkansas Democrat* and she called me for confirmation of it. Loathe to admit this new look for our once solid front, yet appreciative of her co-operation through my years as chairman of the WEC, I was honest with her, but I asked her to consider my confidence as off the record, and she concurred. It was not until after the election that I learned of a circular which had been distributed near the polls. Had I been apprised of this earlier, I would have welcomed the chance to publicize my support of Dr. Jackson and of our own Sara Murphy who was opposing Everett Tucker. This was the leaflet which helped defeat Sara but failed to elect Dr. Jackson:

TO THE THINKING CITIZENS OF LITTLE ROCK

WHY ARE SOME OF OUR NEGRO LEADERS SUPPORTING
THE WOMEN'S EMERGENCY COMMITTEE CANDIDATES
FOR THE SCHOOL BOARD WHEN THIS ORGANIZATION
REFUSES TO ENDORSE OUR OWN CANDIDATE

DR. M. A. JACKSON
WHILE PUBLICLY ENDORSING
DR. JACKSON'S OPPONENT? WE FEEL
that this is a "Slap in the Negro's Face!"

WE FEEL THAT OUR LEADERS HAVE NO LEGITIMATE REASON
FOR THIS ENDORSEMENT SINCE THEY ARE NOT IN ANY WAY
OBLIGATED to this GROUP THEIR CANDIDATE HAS NO
RECORD OF SERVICE WHICH HAS BENEFITED THE NEGRO
DIRECTLY OR INDIRECTLY.

WE HAVE WORKED UNTIRINGLY WITH THE WOMEN'S
EMERGENCY COMMITTEE SINCE THE BEGINNING OF THEIR
ORGANIZATION. HOWEVER, IN VIEW OF THE STAND THEY
ARE TAKING IN OPPOSING DR. JACKSON, WE FEEL THAT

THE NEGRO COMMUNITY SHOULD NOT SUPPORT THE W.E.C. CANDIDATE.

WE, THE UNDERSIGNED – CITIZENS' COMMITTEE URGE THE COMMUNITY TO SUPPORT DR. M. A. JACKSON
A HUMANITARIAN, CIVIC LEADER AND WORKER
AND
EVERETT TUCKER
WHO HAS WORKED TO KEEP OUR PUBLIC SCHOOLS OPEN COMPLYING WITH THE SUPREME COURT DECISION ON DESEGREGATION

CITIZENS' COMMITTEE
Headed by REV. F.T. EVANS – Little Rock:

REV. N. K. CURRY	REV. A. BOSLEY
MRS. J. H. CLAYBORN	MRS. D.N. CLAYBORN
ROY TAYLOR	MURRY PUGH
REV. C. H. HILL	REV A. C. GRANE
REV. W. R. VAUGHN	GENERAL JONES
REV. V. W. NELSON	MRS. ARETHA HOLMES
LINZIE GRIFFIN	ROBERT INGRAM
ARCHIE ELLIS JR.	H. T. JONES
REV. JAMES S. ALLEN	DAVID CLAYBORN MRS. M.
S. McELROY	

DR. M. A. JACKSON .... **X**
MR. EVERETT TUCKER .... **X**

To return to the initial chapter in the WEC-Dr. Jackson story: That evening in the fall of 1959 Mrs. Terry and I asked for no decision from Dr. Jackson or his friends, and none was made in our presence. As we left, Dr. and Mrs. Freeman followed us to the door and Dr. Freeman, in hostile bitterness, demanded, "Why do you always have to come to our houses? Why are we never invited to yours?"

I was completely sincere when I answered him but I sensed that he did not believe me. "You are welcome in my home at any time," I assured him. "I would have asked you there tonight, gladly, but I live some twenty miles from here and I thought it easier for me to come to you than to have all of you make the long trip into the country." He showed no signs of being mollified and I knew that it was up to me to earn his trust. I am gratified to be able to write that in the years to come we became friends.

Mrs. Terry made an immediate effort to avert this threatening schism. She invited Dr. and Mrs. Freeman to join her and her family for dessert and coffee and an evening's visit in her home. That they went was, I felt, a graceful apology, especially since our meeting in their home had proved successful for us. Three days following it, I phoned Dr. Jackson. He said he had decided "after soul searching" not to file. We talked of the necessity for a biracial group and he evinced keen interest. I made him another promise: that I would do everything I could to achieve the fruition of this idea. After all, although I did not tell him so then, that was only a meager aspect of my intent when I first sat down to talk with Mrs. Terry and Velma Powell that fateful afternoon in the fall of 1958.

The need for this liaison was ever more evident. I had received a letter from a Washington, D.C. friend who had long been interested on the Little Rock situation. In part it read:

I do not know anybody else there that I trust sufficiently to give this information to so I pass it on to you.

I have received information which I believe to be reliable, indicating the School Board's attorney, Herschel Friday (formerly attorney for the Governor) has proposed to the Little Rock School Board, and it has agreed, that they select under the Arkansas placement law only those colored children whose background, economic status, etc., would indicate that they could not stand up under the pressure which will be exerted on them in the coming school year. In this way the School Board can create the impression that they are endeavoring to comply with the court's order to accept colored children, but the colored children themselves do not want to go sufficiently to withstand the pressure and drop out and return to the colored schools. By this means they will avoid integration of schools in Little Rock through no apparent fault of the School Board. This pattern follows the Mansfield, Texas example which has always been referred to by the segregationists there in Little Rock as a way to avoid desegregation in the public schools. In Mansfield, Texas, the Governor intervened as "preservator" of the peace by sending the Texas Rangers when there was trouble, and the colored children withdrew.

I do not know what the answer is except to urge the colored families to bear up under the organized intimidation which the Governor will soon bring to bear through his front organizations of the Mothers League and Citizens Council. I do not know what you can do about it but perhaps you can warn the appropriate individuals in Little Rock.

With increasing concern we invited Russell Matson, Vice President of the Little Rock School Board, to explain to our November open meeting the School Board's application of the pupil placement act. The Board was "using the pupil placement law just exactly like the law says, treating all students alike," he assured us. In assigning students to schools, the Board took into account not only the "emotional impact" on both the individual student and groups of students but "also the total impact on the community in line with the original U.S. Supreme Court decision calling for desegregation with all deliberate speed."

He continued: "I think that phrase has wide interpretation. And in my opinion you can't just destroy a community by indiscriminately assigning students to various schools.... We treated all students and parents alike in the assignment hearings. We had the school psychologist test both Negro and white students from a psychological standpoint and we also gave academic tests. Probably the percentage of Negroes to whom we gave the tests was higher because about three times as many white students as Negroes applied for reassignment."

"In some cases it might be a factor, but other reasons carry much more weight. We had to consider the welfare and adjustment problems of the individual. And we placed quite a bit of weight on the fact that children do better work when they are among friends. Whether we like it or not, there are different scholastic averages between schools and between groups within any one school. And it is highly possible that academically a child could do better in one school than another; we took that into consideration also. And a child's attitude toward attending school and his approach to school work as well as his personality were among factors which we considered." *(Arkansas Democrat, November 3, 1959)*

It was perfectly obvious that a number of our members took a dim view of that statement that all students had been treated alike, and they suspected the tactics of the School Board to be less than just. Some of the questions flung at Mr. Matson were sharp, a few little short of rude. He appeared unruffled as he stood by the precepts he had outlined, but I was uneasy that he might harbor resentment of this unsympathetic reception. It was my custom to write a thank you letter to our speakers, but this time I felt it wise to be reassured of his humor following this barrage of invidious queries. We needed every friend we could find on the School Board. I phoned him to express our gratitude for his giving us time that afternoon. "Oh, I enjoyed it," he answered cheerfully, and he made it sound as though he meant it.

Our night meetings always followed the daytime ones, and if the same speaker could not attend both, we arranged for another to bring the same information to the evening session. This night group was as constant as the members who had more time to give to our demanding program, and the attendance now numbered about seventy-five. Margaret Hunt, a teacher, had been the first chairwoman of the night meetings and now our devoted friend, Chris Raetz, took over this organizational job. I did not always attend since my long night drives into town worried Joe, but I did go occasionally to keep in close touch, speaking on the background and purposes of the WEC at one meeting, and serving on a panel at another, listening, learning and answering any questions I could.

In August, the County Equalization Board had asked the Little Rock School Board to reduce the school millage, in spite of the financial plight caused by the withholding of state funds during the 1958-1959 school year. I do not know who sponsored the eventual decision, but when we learned that the School Board election ballot was to include a vote to retain our present millage of forty or reduce it to thirty-eight, we knew we had more work to do. Also, we determined to support a friendly candidate for the County Board of Education and fifty-one of our women signed the petition for Dr. Calvin J. Dillaha.

With election day, December 1, 1959, drawing near and so much at stake, I began to give my days to the seemingly endless task of checking our cards listing the qualified voters. Before this, I had spent most of my time on policy, contacts and letters, all parts of the program which needed to be carried forward and beyond the election. On Thanksgiving I took home with me the cards from one precinct to check the phone numbers from a criss-cross directory, and many another woman spent that holiday this same way.

As I have noted, the Committee for the Peaceful Operation of the Public Schools, a small group of men from the STOP organization, called a meeting for 7:30 on the night of November 24 at the Skyway room of the Hotel Lafayette. A gratifyingly large crowd appeared, many of them our members and their husbands and families. Gaston Williamson, the chairman, praised the WEC, saying the committee was "all honed and polished up again" to work in the election. I don't know where he thought we had been since May, but if he had omitted the word "again" he spoke truly. Scores, no, hundreds of women had persistently honed and polished. Arrangements had been made for poll watchers and for standbys; precinct secretaries had been secured and, under each one of these, there were workers standing ready to attempt to cover the entire city. We had studied the strengths and weaknesses in the May vote, and our organization to use this knowledge was thorough.

The Committee for the Peaceful Operation of the Public Schools installed in our office four unlisted telephones and women manned these for the week preceding December 1. We called all "friendly" qualified voters as indicated by the code on the cards which had been so laboriously labeled and filed, and with each completed call, marked the code letters on the card of the voter contacted to signify the response.

Four informational, inspirational bulletins called GOLIGHTS were mimeographed during this hectic week and were mailed to each worker involved in the election process. Once more our office hummed with frantic activity. And this efficient, tireless effort paid off in full. Everett Tucker won over Mrs. Morrison 8,878 to 4,162; Frank Mackey won over Mrs. Ray 8,882 to 4,082. Dr. Dillaha had a total of 7,891 votes against John K. Shamburger, an attorney, who polled 4,642 votes. The reduction of the millage was defeated 8,593 to 4,354.

On December 8th, we sent out another pink newsletter to congratulate and thank every member. "We have happily passed one more emergency," we affirmed, "and everyone deserves a holiday vacation, but the office will be open until Friday, December 18th. With the New Year, we'll go back to work with renewed zeal... *Have a wonderful Christmas and a truly New Year.* Come to the January 5th meeting and report in at the office for our new projects."

We composed a grateful Christmas letter, and again thousands of these went out of the state with Christmas greetings sent to friends by our members. "Little Rock is a different city this Christmas," we began happily. Once again we received notices of quotes of this in the press in many other cities and we were proud to know of countless favorable comments on the accomplishments of the WEC.

Our Christmas holidays began on December 19th. I felt deeply grateful for the success of this year, especially so to each one of our members in the WEC who had worked so faithfully. I wished I could tell them of my gratitude in ways other than through the newsletter. Very few of them had ever been in our home, so Joe and I decided to have an open house on December 27th. I tried to include all the women, and their husbands, with whom I'd had any personal contact, and the list ran to hundreds. I wished it might have included the entire membership.

One project that fall which I must not fail to mention, was not sponsored by the WEC but we took great interest in it and many of our members contributed countless hours to it. Anne Helvenston suggested to our executive committee: "Why not make a survey to compare the registration in the high schools with normal years?" We liked this idea but decided that the School Board election must come first and probably would absorb all of our energies. Happily, the Seven College Conference group became involved and Mary Jane Gates, a Vassar graduate, promoted the plan. On December 8th, the *Arkansas Gazette* reported the findings:

> An estimated 1,142 of the 4,279 young persons expected to attend the Little Rock public high schools this year are not there.. 446 of the missing students were attending other Arkansas high schools. . , 289 were in high schools outside Arkansas, 253 were not in school at all, 60 were in college and 93 were not accounted for. One had died. Mr. L.C. Henderson, Supervisor of Secondary Education, said he believed that most of the 735 attending other high schools were there because of the uncertainty of the Little Rock school situation at

> the end of the school year last spring. Many
> already were enrolled in other schools, hav-
> ing gone there during the year the Little Rock
> schools were closed to avoid desegregation,
> and they decided to continue there instead
> of risking another year without schools in
> Little Rock. The 60 in college probably had
> to pass special examinations to get in. Prac-
> tically all of them would have been high
> school seniors this year, although about four
> would have been only juniors, the survey
> showed. The 253 not attending school prob-
> ably had gone to work, married or for some
> other reason had dropped out.

We hoped that Mr. Faubus pondered these figures long and soberly.

One last episode in late 1959 deserves mention.
On September 28, 1959, I received a telegram from
the Loretta Young Show, at the time one of the
country's most popular television shows. The Hollywood producers of the show asked if I would be interested in Loretta Young doing a dramatization of
the activities of the WEC. Of course I was. Two
months ensued, and I wrote, reviewed and sent back
and forth to Miss Young's story editor a number of
reports about the WEC.

I was very pleased that the WEC would be featured in a national telecast with a star such as Loretta
Young. Unfortunately, my enthusiasm got the better of me, and I foolishly informed WEC members at
our November 3, 1959 open meeting about the pros-

pects for the show. Probably we had a spy in our midst that day, because soon afterwards anti-integration newspapers and the Capital Citizens Council began a lengthy diatribe against me and the WEC, and amazingly enough, even against Loretta Young for planning a feature on the WEC. The sponsors of Miss Young's Show, the Benson and Hedges Company, and Miss Young herself received numerous, irresponsible and wildly exaggerated letters from self-proclaimed segregationists who threatened national boycotts if the WEC story was presented. *Time Magazine* got wind of the uproar and asked me for an interview. Fearful of fanning the flames, I demurred, but it was too late. By late December, it was all too clear the pressures on the Hollywood staff had effectively stopped the Loretta Young Show from proceeding with plans to dramatize the WEC's battle for public education. Though in the end nothing came of it, this episode created a new awareness in me of both the dangers and rewards of publicity, and especially the power of television to capture public attention.

Nine

Politics Is Not My Forte

January 1960 started with flattering encourage
ment as a friend sent me the latest issue of
The Progressive with its warm Holiday Greetings including: "To Mrs. Joe E. (sic) Brewer, chairman, and her WEC of Little Rock, who showed that
city's business leaders the way to forthright action
against Governor Orval Faubus' destructive policies."
Naturally, I was pleased but realistically I faced up
to our goading failure. Our emergency program to
open our high schools had been achieved but our
long term program to help solve the social problem
of interracial relations seemed stagnant.

The necessity for a civic interracial committee
plagued me. Gaston Williamson, the Chairman of
the Committee for the Peaceful Operation of the
Schools, thought we might as well give up on that
score. He was positive the city would do nothing
about it, nor would the Chamber of Commerce. "The

city board won't," he argued, "because four members are up for re-election next December."

Grainger Williams and Will Mitchell affirmed this assessment of the Chamber of Commerce. "There's too much opposition on the board," they reported. "Even the moderates are convinced the good they can do transcends the good such a committee could do." They were apprehensive that the general reaction to the formation of an interracial committee would be a renewed surge of intolerance. "Look at Dollarway (Pine Bluff, Arkansas)," they cautioned us. "It's a hot bed of intolerance now, and just five years ago there was a Negro on the school board there."

Adolphine Terry wasn't convinced, despite her deep respect for these men. She invited a small group to her home for lunch on February 14th: Billy Rector, Everett Tucker, Bishop Brown, Grainger Williams, Gaston Williamson, Thelma Babbitt, Irene Samuel and myself. The theme was "What can we do?" Both Rector and Tucker were adamant: "Do nothing!" Rector's defeat for the School Board rankled and he chose to blame the WEC. Our disgrace as integrationists, as so effectively affirmed by Mr. Faubus, had contaminated him. The meeting became increasingly vocal and — to us — exceedingly frustrating. Inevitably and unfortunately, the talk turned to the schools, and Mr. Tucker felt all was well, *splendidly under control.* (Italics mine.) We women struggled to project the overall picture of the separate and unequal smoldering climate. Bishop Brown solemnly assured us that things would get far worse, and he agreed that "something needs to be done,"

but he offered no advice. There was a general cho-
rus as the men were polled. "Yes, something needs
to be done. We don't know what, but *not what you
suggest.*"

And our schools? Yes, they had been open now
for over five months, but for how much longer? Governor Faubus had pushed through the 1959 General Assembly Joint Resolution No. 5, which would
appear on the statewide ballot in the general election in November of this 1960 as Proposed Amendment No. 52. The next nine months could birth a
monstrous law capable of destroying our public
school system, fomenting ignorance and hate, driving our best minds to other environs, thwarting industrial development, dooming Arkansas to the reality of its backwoods image. It seemed to me now
that the reopening of the schools was only another
minor political victory and our major fight lay ahead.
Since this must be a statewide one, there were no
moments or energies to lose.

Our February meeting made it all to clear that
my immediate responsibility lay in pulling our group
together for this new objective. Only eight women
showed up! Mrs. Terry was out of town; no effort
had been made to remind our membership of the
date. Were we complacent now — or tired — or just
forgetful? My notes of that day indicate we had sent
out 3,000 Christmas letters to out-of-town friends.
Of our third run of our *Little Rock Report,* only sixteen copies remained. The Seven College Conference
survey had indicated the enrollment in our high
schools was 1,142 under normal. Derogatory, anony-

mous "fan mail" to our office and to our publicized officers was still heavy. Surely all we needed was, as there had been in 1959, one positive goal. How could we escape it — the defeat of this proposed "school destruction" amendment No. 52? This must be our paramount objective despite inescapable involvement in the Democratic primary on July 26 and the run-off election on August 9.

Our first move was to go on record as unalterably opposed to this proposed amendment. We were the first group to announce this position, but our declaration was too early for reaction from the press or the public. Approached for cooperation, Forrest Rozzell, Executive Secretary of the Arkansas Education Association, advised that his organization would plan a master campaign against No. 52 but would take no action until after the primaries in July. This seemed to me a foolish delay, and I did not understand his reasoning until months later. The WEC had no funds for a crash campaign, but we believed in action *now*. We immediately began to plan, to study, to make contacts, to proselytize. We resolved to quit talking to each other and to try to inform the grocer, the mailman, the plumber, the milkman, the laundryman, everyone with whom we had any contact.

Our initial action was to arrange for copies of the entire proposed amendment, but I wondered how many would bother to study the hidden meanings of its thirteen sections. We could not, at that time, know how this "public school amendment" would be summarized on the ballot in November, and we had little faith that its synopsis, printed on the ballot as prepared by the Faubus forces, would be worded in any but a most negatively persuasive manner. Time proved our suspicions well founded.

With the advice of friendly attorneys, we drafted a three page study of "Some Implications of Proposed Amendment No, 52." This lengthy description was used extensively within the WEC, but realizing that most voters had no patience with three legal cap pages of material couched in legal terms, we reduced this to a one page simplified version of the most salient points (see Appendix 31). Once more Jo Menkus performed yeomanly duty at the mimeograph machine.

These materials we gladly supplied in quantity to any individual or group throughout the state. In addition, we offered a speaker for any meeting anywhere, calling attention to this threat to our public education. To this end, we trained groups of women in study, question and answer sessions. Avoid politics, we urged and *never* mention the racial issue. Know the facts about the amendment and our school system and adhere strictly to these facts. We organized buzz sessions by setting up coffees and coke parties in homes in every precinct in Little Rock. Specific schedules were arranged with speakers accepting definite appointments. Sometimes these sessions were frustrating, with so few attending, but we tried to maintain the morale of the speakers who were devoting so much of their time to this effort. *Every vote counts!* Often I repeated the story of my father's first political race in Little Rock. Too modest to vote for himself and unwilling to vote for his opponent, he went out of the city over election day and filed no absentee ballot. The vote was a tie.

A corps of women made numerous trips within the state. A few instances are prominent in my memory: Billie Wilson bravely accepted invitations to cities in eastern Arkansas where resistance to desegregation clouded the issues so emotionally that our cause needed calm, factual but charismatic elucidation. When, for personal reasons, I was unable to accept the invitation, three of our women drove to Conway for a night meeting with the Alpha Chi Society at College. By request of Mrs. E.A. Stuck of Jonesboro, the state president of AAUW, I attended their regional meetings in Arkadelphia and in Harrison to talk about the grave risks in Amendment 52.

Gradually, many groups joined the battle and each declaration encouraged us. But where was the governor — and why? His statements were evasive. In June, he told the press (*Arkansas Gazette,* June 8): "I have never advocated abolishing the public school system." When Joint Resolution No. 5, which became the proposed Amendment No. 52, was pushed through the 1959 General Assembly, it "was the best course at the time. If conditions have changed," he told the Committee on Political Education of the state AFL-CIO (*Arkansas Gazette, June 6, 1960*), "then the people of the state can reject the Amendment. If they have remained the same, I think it would be good to have it."

As late as August 23, after a meeting with an Arkansas Education Association Committee, the governor twice made one point: that he "had not been asked to take a stand for or against and that he hadn't volunteered to do so." (*Arkansas Gazette,* August 24, 1960). This meeting was attended by Dr. Hugh L. Mills of Hot Springs, School Superintendent and President of the state A.E.A., by Clarence E. Bell, state Senator from Parkin, and by Marvin Bird of Earle, Chairman of the state Board of Education. Dr. Mills published a wary statement announcing that the A.E.A. had not taken an official stand on the proposed amendment. "The official A.E.A. position has not been formulated and will not be until after this discussion with Mr. Faubus is analyzed," Dr. Mills is quoted as saying.

About this time, the Committee on Constitutional Government sent a letter to Governor Faubus asking him to back the proposed constitutional amendment. The committee, with offices in Forrest City in the eastern part of the state, announced it would campaign actively for the adoption of the amendment. The *Arkansas Gazette* quoted from their letter: "There are a number of school districts in eastern Arkansas which will vitally need the provisions of Amendment 52 to prevent amalgamation of the races. We know of no other legal instruments which they can use which will effectively avoid this catastrophe."

Thus we found it difficult to feel any firm confidence in our ultimate victory, even when Dr. Mills, at long last, following a meeting of the Board of Directors of the A.E.A. on August 29, the primaries and the run-off election now history, passed out copies of a four page mimeographed statement declaring that organization's opposition to the amendment. Although, we were assured, *the A.E.A. was just fighting No. 52, not Faubus.* Now we knew and were disdainful, but at least their move against the amendment was overt. Irene Samuel and I, rather to our surprise, were invited to meet with Forrest Rozzell, Executive Secretary of the A.E.A. and Joshua K. Shepherd, a Little Rock civic leader whom Mr. Rozzell had chosen to head the Committee Against Amendment No. 52. Later, we and Pat House were publicly listed among the 48 names of a statewide steering committee. On September 24, about 500 persons attended a session at the Robinson Auditorium in Little Rock to hear Eugene R. Warren, attorney for the A.E.A. and for the Classroom Teachers, outline the proposal's pitfalls. It was good to have him vocal in the school crisis.

Gradually, other organizations spoke out. The Little Rock branch of AAUW called No. 52 a disaster. The Pulaski County Bar Association rejected No. 52 by a vote of sixty-five to four. The Little Rock School Board, with only J.H. Cottrell dissenting, issued a statement opposing No. 52. Former Governor Sidney McMath spoke effectively on a half hour TV program on the eve of election day. But on October 28, Governor Faubus had broken his long silence in a thirty-minute speech on TV in which he made a strong defense of his school closing amendment. As usual he played the racial harp:

> Recently I saw the names of a state steering committee appointed to oppose Amend-

ment 52. There were the names of a lot of
fine people on this steering committee,
many of whom have been misled. Some of
the names should be quite revealing to you.
There is the name of Tom Dearmore of
Mountain Home. He has been writing editorials along the Ashmore line since 1957
which have been published in the *Gazette.*
There is the name of Mrs. Joe Brewer of
Scott. She is a member and for a long time
has been the leader of the Women's Emergency Committee of Little Rock, the most
ardent integration organization in the state.
Other names on this committee can be
found on the list of the Women's Emergency
Committee members and the old STOP
group in Little Rock. Now this should indicate to you — the people of the state —
that the shock troops of the opposition to
Amendment 52 come from the old well-
known integration group.

Joe and I heard this as we dined in a downtown
restaurant and we went straight away to the Western Union office to send Tom Dearmore a "Welcome
to our club" telegram. But we were worried by
Faubus' coming out for the amendment, and so, as
the *Gazette* editorialized on November 10th: "The 3
to 1 vote against Amendment 52 (in the November
general election) was by all odds the most gratifying
single demonstration of the people's will."

Amendment No. 52 was defeated 247,804 to
83,900. Proposed Amendments No. 50 and No. 51,
caught in the backwash against Amendment No. 52,
were also defeated. Amendment No. 50 would have

doubled the permissive ceiling on constitutional salaries from governor down to county and municipal
offices. No. 51 would have increased the municipal
levy for capital improvements from five mills to ten
mills and the tax for general purposes from five to
ten mills. This measure also would leave to each
municipality's voters the final say about taxes. Governor Faubus' reaction was philosophical: "It looks
like all are gone. Well, we can live without them." In
the strange way of politics he had been elected over-
whelmingly to his fourth term as governor.

Throughout this 1960 summer and fall, despite
our concentration on defeating Amendment 52 on
November 7, ineluctably the school issue became
political and politics struck deeply into the cohe-
sion of the WEC. Without warning, Irene Samuel
moved herself and needed materials out of the WEC
offices in order to manage a headquarters in support of Joe C. Hardin in his campaign against Orval
E. Faubus for the governorship. The primaries were
to be held on July 26 that year and the general
election date coincided with that in which Amendment 52 would be on the ballot, November 7. I could
not blame the many women who followed Mrs.
Samuel excitedly, for Mr. Faubus obviously was *the*
issue in so many of our minds. Nor could I resent
the plea that I absent myself from the Hardin campaign.

Suddenly I found myself in a somewhat unnerv-
ing situation, left rather lonely in the WEC office,
thrust into the position of making political decisions
about county races. The work of our women in the

school board elections and the STOP campaign had given us some status as a pressure group. Candidates sought our approval and it became my obligation to interview them, hopefully to form a wise judgment which might influence the WEC's selection. Some instances were clear cut, for our primary test must be the firm support of public education. To prove our case concerning the incumbents seeking re-election, with a great deal of work involving cautious research both of 1958-59 legislation and voting records, organization of material and diagramming, we developed a chart which provided positive evidence of each Pulaski County legislator's stand for or against our public schools. Meticulously sketched by Ruth Hrishekesan, this chart was used widely in the summer campaign of 1960.

It was probably my personal apprehension that the WEC might become *only* a political pressure group that persuaded our board to decline public sanction of any particular candidate at this time. We had consolidated our convictions almost unanimously but believed it the wiser course to let each woman express her opinion as an individual. To be helpful, we mimeographed many hundreds of sheets highlighting the candidates for various offices, and, excepting the race for representative from the Fifth District in which we could not resist opposing our old arch-foe Dale Alford, we left it to the WEC member to insert her own choice and so advise her friends.

Many women came to the office for these bulletins to mail personally to friends and acquaintances, and usually they sought advice as to our predilections. I tried to temper all counseling with objectivity and reason, with forceful emphasis on public education, but there were days of doubt, and there were explosive developments.

In the governor's race, there could be no hesitation or vacillation. Joe C. Hardin had to be our man, if only because of his unequivocal support of public education and his prompt and persistent opposition to Amendment No. 52. And I think few of us gave second thoughts to any of the other candidates for governor except Orval E. Faubus.

Mr. Hardin's campaign was marked by sober, sane, dignified, honest and dull statements. A remarkably fine, sincere man, he lacked that political halo, charisma. Orval Faubus, on the other hand, had learned the political magic of extravagant allegations, statistically unfounded but exciting, moving. When Little Rock was once more terrified by the threatened bombing of an old dormitory building at Philander Smith College, at that time a Negro institution, and an explosion which rocked a Negro residential neighborhood some twelve blocks from the college, Mr. Faubus seized upon this emotional moment. In his talks at Siloam Springs and at Fayetteville, as part of an attack upon his opponent, Joe C. Hardin, the Governor cast racially imbued aspersions on Mrs. D.D. Terry. He said that Hardin began his campaign at Little Rock with a series of tea parties, one of which was at Mrs. Terry's home. "Now who is Mrs. Terry?" he asked. "She is a fine old lady but she is the strongest integrationist you ever saw." Mr. Faubus added that Mrs. Terry believed not only in public school integration but also in intermarriage of the races. He went on to explain that Mrs. Terry was a founder of the Women's Emergency Committee for Public schools, "the integrationist front in Little Rock."

Mrs. Terry issued a personal statement in response to the Governor's gallant sally, and the press carried it in full:

> At my advanced age (77) I am hardly interested in becoming a campaign issue but since Governor Faubus has to make me one, my family and I feel that I should reply.
>
> I voted twice for Governor Faubus. The first time I deplored the fact that he was being attacked as a Communist when the country was suffering from the effect of the McCarthy reign. After he took office I invited one-hundred Little Rock women to meet Mrs. Faubus. The second time he ran against Judge (Jim) Johnson, Governor Faubus reiterated that the school situation was a local issue; if elected, the various communities could solve their own problems. The fall of 1957, my husband and I were visiting our son in Colorado Springs when the news broke over TV that Governor Faubus, our chief constitutional officer, had used troops, not to uphold the law and the Constitution of our country, but to defy them.
>
> We have spent our lives in working for the advancement of our city and state, as our fathers did before us. When Little Rock became an evil word around the world, I felt

that my own world had collapsed. Before the Women's Emergency Committee was formed, I wrote a personal letter to Governor Faubus stating that with his great ability and position, he could solve this racial problem, not only for Arkansans but the nation as well. That he could make himself not notorious, but immortal. I even quoted Deuteronomy 30:19: "I have set before you life and death, blessings and cursing; therefore choose life..." Perhaps he never received the letter; it was never answered. But he chose to be recorded in history, not as a great leader, but as a Talmadge, a Bilbo, a demagogue. He chose ultimate death.

Mr. Faubus ignored this and continued blithely on his speaking tour, repeating his innuendo against Mrs. Terry and the WEC, and adding another facet. Early in April, Mrs. Shirin Fozdar, an Asiatic Indian from Singapore, making a world tour, stopped briefly in Little Rock. President of the Baha'i Assembly of Southeast Asia, sponsored by the Singapore Council of Women and a guest of the United States government, she had made a special request of our State Department to include Little Rock in her itinerary, and while here addressed a small group of Negro women and a number of ministers. In a press interview she spoke plainly of Little Rock's "truly short-sighted policy in failing to be aware of the effect of racial events here," and she added, "If America does not treat the colored people with dignity, and this country is one that believes in God, why the Negroes will turn to the godless communism to be treated with dignity." Hearing of the efforts of the WEC, she asked to visit our office and arrived one morning when we were holding a training session for speakers on the proposed Amendment 52. She was delightfully courteous with the beautiful manners of the East, but she was rushed and had no opportunity to address even these few of our members. Yet Mr. Faubus told his audience that the WEC had invited Mrs. Fozdar to Little Rock to speak at one of its meetings, and he added that Mrs. Fozdar had advocated racial inter-marriage in one of our national magazines, and this proved that the WEC was an integrationist organization.

Following Mr. Faubus' speech which had been telecast, Mrs. Terry sent a further statement to the Governor: "... While I believe in complying with the law, I am not for forcible integration nor have I ever advocated interracial marriage. For your information, I did not meet the Asian visitor to whom you referred in your address this evening." Incensed by the Governor's ridiculous involvement of Mrs. Terry in his campaign, I felt constrained to answer Mr. Faubus for once, even though indirectly and I sent this statement to the press:

> The Women's Emergency Committee had no part in inviting Mrs. Fozdar to visit Little Rock. It is our understanding that she came to our city under the auspices of the International Educational Exchange Service of the Department of State under a leader grant. She was sponsored, at the request

of the Committee on Leaders and Specialists, by Mrs. Felix Arnold, president of the Little Rock League of Women Voters.

She visited our office at a time a committee of six or seven speakers studying the defeat of the proposed Amendment 52 was in session. She made no statement other than her interest in our program to preserve our public schools and her profound concern that Little Rock had become the symbol of iniquity throughout the world. She made no appearance before the WEC meetings, either the board or the monthly open meeting.

Our entire membership was outraged by the Governor's attack on Mrs. Terry, and inspired and organized by Eleanor Reid, 62 civic leaders and prominent citizens wrote statements filled with expressions of admiration and devotion to "our great lady."

"Rare."

"A distinguished person."

"Noble."

"A southern lady."

"One of our great women."

These statements were given to the press and many of them appeared in a loyal salute to Adolphine Fletcher Terry. I suspect that Mr. Faubus only smiled. He was well aware that all of these tributes were true but he had successfully planted the racial issues in the public mind. My records show that the vote for governor in the July 26th primary proved he knew his people:

With 2242 boxes out of 2353 (statewide) and 88 out of 91 boxes (in our own Pulaski County) reporting on July 27, 1960:

	Statewide	Pulaski County
Bennett	55,444 votes	4,035 votes
Faubus	226,748	26,216
Hardin	63,609	16,467
Millsap	11,520	3,224
Williams	29,051	601

Although the office volunteers, reduced in numbers by the Hardin race, already had more work than we could say grace over, we became somewhat involved in other campaigns.

James Coates, for instance, brought Robert Hays Williams to the WEC office to ask our help in his race against the freshman incumbent, Dale Alford, for Representative to the United States Congress from Arkansas' Fifth District. We had no choice but to support Mr. Williams against Dr. Alford, since Mr. Williams professed to being a staunch advocate of public schools. However, I explained that much of our woman-power was over-worked in the governor's race, I did give them a synopsis of our methods of action in campaigns and offered to supply what help we could. They needed someone to co-ordinate their headquarters, and I suggested Polly Farris (Mrs. Norman Farris). They were fortunate to interest her and she gave full time to this campaign. Mr. Williams conducted a vigorous race but he was no match for

Mr. Faubus' understudy and he seemed unprepared personally for his first political defeat. When I visited his office the night of the primaries, he was completely uncommunicative, and Polly Farris, reminiscing with me some time later, admitted she'd had not one word from him following that election day.

Chalk up two major losses for the WEC — Mr. Hardin and Mr. Williams — but in the seven contested races for the state legislature, four of "our men" were winners: Ellis Fagan for the Senate; Harry W. Carter, Jim Brandon and Sterling Cockrill for the House. There are a few entertaining stories about those races.

By June 30th, the executive board of the WEC reached the delayed decision that it might be wise to reach our membership with a positive statement on the political situation, and we issued a brief bulletin:

> The results of our survey showed almost unanimously that you wish to support candidates for the state legislature committed to the preservation of our public schools. We have tried to investigate the voting records, the public statements and the reputations of various candidates and it is our opinion that the following men will maintain a "general, suitable and efficient system" of free public schools in the state of Arkansas:
>
> For Senator, Pulaski County:
>   Position #2   Ellis M. Fagan
>   Position #3   W.H. (Bill) Donham
>   E.C. Shelby
> For Representative, Pulaski County:
>   Position #1   Louis Nalley

Position #2	Harry W. Carter
	J.M. (Jim) Harrison
Position #5	Jim Brandon
Position #6	J.M. Collins

We were supporting Sterling Cockrill for Position No. 8 against Mrs. Floyd B. Peck who was no friend of ours, but Mr. Cockrill expressed a wish to be ignored by us and perhaps we should have analyzed more carefully the effects of this on his victory. Ellis Fagan, successful in his race for the Senate, was courageous in referring to the WEC in an ad taking exception to Mr. Langford's having sent letters to us by very special delivery:

> Do you, Mr. Langford, believe in a Police state? Why did you, as City Director, send policemen to deliver letters when a postman would have done it for four cents? Were you trying to make this fine group of women feel like criminals? Or is this your idea of economy in government?

T.E. "Tom" Tyler's amusing pictorial ad with each of his four opponents pointing to him with the accusation "Segregationist," in classifying the WEC with the *Arkansas Gazette,* the NAACP, and Daisy Bates, depicted us as an elderly, fat, bespectacled Helen Hokinson character. The results of this race in the primaries are rather interesting:

James (Jimmy) Joyner	5,615
Harry Carter	14,440
T.E. (Tom) Tyler	15,632
William M. Byrd	3,213
J.M. Harrison	10,755

Mr. Carter was the one candidate to call me to express his thanks for the help of the WEC. But J.M. Harrison, whom I saw at the Williams headquarters the night of the primaries, startled me as I attempted to express condolences to him. "You are the one who defeated me," he accused bitterly. The public image of the WEC obviously had many facets.

Jim Brandon, who had helped us with public relations problems in the very first weeks of the existence of the WEC, had political ambitions. He brought to a meeting of our executive board early in 1960 his intention to run against Mrs. Gordon P. (Willie) Oates for Position No. 5 in the House of the state Legislature, and he asked our help. He produced a list of probable expenses totaling $2,100.00 with the intimation that the WEC might cover this. Another facet of our reputation? Of course, we had no such resources but we did agree to help in every way we could. Many of our members were friends and admirers of Willie Oates who was an ardent club woman, often in news and society items in the women's section of the papers. To make clear and logical our position, we made available a statement: "Why we are opposed to another term for Willie Oates," based on her support of Raney High School and on her voting record. We obtained a list of young people to help Jim and his wife at supermarkets on Saturdays, to distribute materials and bumper stickers. We found places where he might erect yard signs. Many of our women addressed and signed postcards for him. Many signed ads in the newspapers. We mimeographed materials for him. We arranged for cars to the polls on election day and organized a battery of women to make phone calls at election time.

The unofficial tabulation of the primaries vote in July showed Jim Brandon had won by 193 votes. Mrs. Oates asked and received the County Democratic Committee's permission for a recount, agreeing to pay the costs of some $1,000.00. Counters would work in eight crews and each candidate was entitled to one observer for each crew. Ninety-one boxes were involved. The WEC found the crews for Jim and they met August 2nd in the Second Division Circuit Court room on the north end of the second floor of the Pulaski County Court House. By noon on Wednesday, Jim had picked up an additional 298 votes, making a difference of 491. The total vote with the recount finished showed Mrs. Oates: 25,429, Mr. Brandon: 25,920. Mrs. Oates, smiling and gracious, took her defeat in good humor, and emphasized that her request for the recount meant no reflection on the honesty or efficiency of the election officials. The *Arkansas Gazette* editorialized that although the recount had not changed the outcome in the legislative race for Position No. 5, it had served the public interest in turning up new evidence to support the need for voting machines. Certainly Mrs. Oates' contention that there were discrepancies in the counting was borne out, even if the discrepancies worked against her. The worst example was in a North Little Rock box where 228 votes apparently got misplaced on election night. Voters in the North Little Rock precinct might reasonably become exercised over the thought that 228 of their votes were never counted in anything except the race for Position No. 5. That there was no secret ballot in Arkansas had long been one of the concerns of the WEC. The need for voting machines became increasingly imperative. We were pleased to have had a small role in stressing this need.

In Position #6 for the House, the choice was between R. Ben Allen and J.M. Collins. Ben Allen, a likable young attorney and legislator, insisted he was at heart in favor of public education despite his record of anti-education votes. These he discounted with the appealing explanation that he had voted yes on most anti-school bills because he knew they would pass anyway and his long suit was in getting along with people. I admired this amiable quality but was not convinced this was the way to win our battle. With due study of his 14 yes votes on bills which we vehemently opposed, and a special memory of his favorable vote on the proposed Amendment 52, I chose to support a comparative unknown, J.M. Collins, who convinced me that he meant his promise to support public schools faithfully and aggressively.

Two wholly unexpected developments weakened our efforts on Jim Collins' behalf. Our good friend, Ted Lamb, obviously needing business desperately, having lost the vast majority of his public relations accounts due to his integrationist stand in the school board, agreed to help Ben Allen and promoted an effective campaign for him. This hurt. Then Russell H. Matson, Jr., Vice President of the Little Rock School Board, wrote a letter praising Allen as a staunch supporter of public schools. Mr. Matson disclaimed knowledge of how the letter was used, but many teachers reported receiving it. To combat this, we rallied together a small force on a Sunday afternoon to mimeograph and mail a letter for Jim Collins detailing Ben Allen's negative voting record on school legislation and promising close cooperation with the teachers in support of public schools. The final count was — for Allen 28,431 votes, for Collins 20,332 votes. We wondered if this indicated how many people really cared about public education.

For me personally, there was a much more significant political incident. On a Sunday afternoon in July, I was invited to the offices of the legal firm of McMath, Leatherman, Woods and Youndahl. There I found Irene Samuel, Pat House and Adolphine Terry in consultation with Henry Woods and Jim Youngdahl, both of whom had befriended the WEC, and with Sheriff Marlin Hawkins of Conway County and Tommy H. Russell who was to face Dan Sprick in the runoff for Position #3 from Pulaski County in the Arkansas Senate. The sheriff's reputation gave me no assurance that he stood for anything the WEC supported, but I knew him to be a political power not only in his own county but in the state. What his relationship to Mr. Russell was, was never made clear, and it was years later that I was told that the McMath firm's hosting this conference was based on a loyal gratitude for Sheriff Hawkins' backing of Sid McMath in his race for governor some years preceding. Tommy Russell I knew to be very close to Governor Faubus; in fact he had been Faubus' aide.

Questions and answers soon established his ignorance of school problems and his alliance with the Faubus train of thought. "What would you do if several Negroes were assigned to the North Little Rock (Mr. Russell's residence) High School?"

"I'd do some gerry mandering." Jim Youngdahl had the grace to try to hide his amusement as he suddenly rushed off into an adjoining office. Sheriff Hawkins centered his appeal for the support of the WEC in flattering observations of Irene's and Pat's political acuity. We must have talked for an hour or so and I finally suggested that we four women adjourn to Mrs. Terry's home to make our decision.

Not one of us had any respect for Dan Sprick who had evidenced his consistent opposition to all we hoped for, but I saw no reason to help his opponent who seemed to be just as surely our adversary. I felt we should stay out of this race entirely. Irene and Pat both felt we should aid Mr. Russell if only because of the apparent interest of the McMath firm. Mrs. Terry was noncommittal. The way to settle this was to poll our board, so I seated myself at Mrs. Terry's phone and one by one dialed a majority of the members of our Executive Committee to ask their reaction. In fairness, I should say that I expressed no bias on my part, merely asking if each member thought the WEC should publicly endorse Tommy Russell, but I was dismayed to have each one say, "Yes" or "It's all right with me." The majority ruled and so our office mailed out a special WEC newsletter for the runoff election:

It seems to the members of the board of the Women's Emergency Committee that the following candidates in the runoff election August 9, if elected, would best serve the interests of public education:

In the Senate
Position #2   Ellis Fagan
Position #3   Tommy H. Russell

In the House of Representatives
Position #2   Harry Carter

I was deeply disturbed by this. It seemed to me that the WEC had completely lost sight of its purpose in endorsing Tommy Russell. In some instances of our acknowledged support of candidates, I'd had vague doubts, but in this case I was positive that Tommy Russell was not our man. If we were to become purely a political pressure group, I knew I was not the one to head it. That Mr. Russell lost to Mr. Sprick in no way influenced my position. It was this episode which directly led to my decision to resign as chairman of the WEC that fall of 1960.

Ten

The Myth of Civil Service

In the very early days of the committee, one of Joe's sisters who had known long years of government employment, tried to caution me. "You think there is no way they can hurt you, but what would happen if Joe lost his job?"

I was shocked. "Why, there is no danger of that," I said confidently. "He is under civil service." Baffled by my innocence, she smiled ruefully and made no further attempt to disillusion me. It took a nightmare to do that.

My second warning came in a quote from Dr. Dale Alford's first television address on September 26, 1958 just before the city-wide election on segregation vs. integration the following day.

I was too preoccupied that busy night to hear this speech and too intent on my hopes to pay any attention to his words anyway, so I was amazed and somewhat amused when in late February,

260

Mr. and Mrs. Joe Robinson and Vivion Lenon Brewer.
Family photograph circa 1959–1960.

1959, Joe brought home a copy of a letter which had been received by Dr. Harold Sterling, the manager of the North Little Rock Veterans Administration Hospital where Joe was the personnel officer:

> Little Rock, Arkansas
> February 16, 1959
>
> Honorable Dale Alford
> House of Representatives
> Washington 25, D.C.
>
> Dear Dr. Alford
>
> Since you are new on the Committee for Civil Service, it would seem there is something you can do about a situation here in Little Rock that should

be corrected. Under the "Hatch Act" an official or his wife (any Civil Service employee for that matter) is prohibited from partisan or political activities. The wife of the Personnel Officer at Fort Roots hospital (Joe Brewer) is head of an organization to force opening of schools on integrated basis. Her activities, of course, are political and to say the least distasteful to the majority of taxpaying citizens in this area. This woman does not have a child in the schools of Little Rock nor does she live in Little Rock. I am quite sure if there were an official in that hospital whose wife was actively working with the "other political side of this question" that he would be severely dealt with. It is time that our public officials respect the "Law of the land" as so many have so piously quoted the integration question as law of the land.

If our government agencies are to be kept full of this sort of activity it is time that our lawmakers "cut their water off" for we certainly need relief on taxes. In so many words, this Personnel Officer, through his wife is "biting the hand that is feeding him" for we are paying a heavy load of taxes (too heavy) and if this is what our civil servants are doing with their time, it is now time to take some of them to the "chopping block."

Many others in this area are concerned about this same situation and are amazed that this would be allowed to continue since it is strictly against our laws.

A copy of this letter is being forwarded to the Manager at Fort Roots.

Sincerely yours,
F.D. Haley, Jr.

Copy Ft. Roots Manager.

Joe obviously took this less lightly than did I and he made a point of securing a ruling on the Hatch Act from the attorney for the Veterans Administration which assured us that my actions in the Women's Emergency Committee to Open Our Schools could not affect his job status.

He also asked me to assemble descriptive materials of the WEC and sought permission from Dr. Sterling to send this file to the Central Office of the VA in Washington, D.C. This permission was refused and although there was no explanation offered, we assumed at that time that Dr. Sterling must think the Haley letter and its implications of no consequence.

Joe had been personnel officer at this hospital since the spring of 1946. On July 15, 1957 he applied for participation in the Management Development Program, which participation was necessary for an employee to be considered for promotional jobs. Since we had many home, family and financial interests in and near Little Rock, he listed the Greater Little Rock area as the only possible site of appointment. For the five necessary references, he named Dr. Sterling, Mr. E.L. Wilbur, the assistant manager and Joe's immediate supervisor who was responsible for his efficiency ratings, Mr. C.M. Fesler of Washington, D.C., formerly the personnel chief in the regional VA office in St. Louis, Dr. Erwin Chappell, director of Professional Education at the Fort Roots Hospital, and Mr. A. Hammann, manager of the Little Rock regional VA office.

In April of 1959, there were rumors that the

North Little Rock and the Little Rock VA Hospitals were to be consolidated. The morale of the employees at Fort Roots was shattered by the fear of job changes and Joe sought information or suggestions from Dr. Sterling which might help quiet the unrest. Dr. Sterling dismissed him curtly with "Mr. Brewer, I'm not in a position to discuss this," but within minutes after Joe returned to his own office, Dr. Sterling called him back and in his most friendly tone admitted, "Yes, Joe, this is what is going to happen. There is to be a consolidation." Joe remarked that he hoped he would continue to be the personnel officer and Dr. Sterling promised him he would recommend him. About this time, Dr. Sterling made a trip to Washington, and on his return he was inexplicably distant to Joe. Suddenly our social life with our friends at Fort Roots was terminated. Although we had partied back and forth over the years with many of the couples at the "Fort" as the VA Hospital is commonly called, we thought little of the cessation of invitations now for our social life was definitely curtailed by my absorption in the work of the WEC. I was much more concerned and puzzled that only two women from the hospital family joined our committee.

The evening of May 19, 1959, Joe looked stricken as I met him at our door. "I'm not going to get it," he told me. Tears came to my eyes as I knew full well: "I've done this to you." He shook his head but with no conviction. A TWX had come from Central Office that day, recommending three names for the personnel officer of the consolidation and Joe's name was not listed. Dr. Sterling had handed this to Joe with the brief comment that Marvin Koch had made it clear that it was against the policy of the VA to substitute or add names, so there was nothing he could do about it. What had happened to Dr. Sterling's recommendation? What had influenced the choice? The three names listed were of men from widely separated states: one from North Carolina who did not ever visit the Fort and apparently evidenced no interest in the job; one from Tennessee who did come, visited with Joe and decided that he didn't want to move his family into the present turmoil in our city; and one from Louisiana who came to see Dr. Sterling but did not call at Joe's office. He was the one who accepted the position: Ray D. Huard, a Catholic who need face no school problem for his children, who would gain a promotion in grade and salary and in prestige as he jumped from a hospital of about 600 beds to one of 2500. How could we blame him, even though this seemed a bitter pill after thirty-two years of government service. Joe was deeply depressed by his failure and began to blame only himself.

The evening of the 22nd of May, as we settled in front of the TV to hear Governor Faubus urge support of "his" school board members in the Recall election scheduled the following day, I tried to rebuild Joe's confidence with the memories of his long and successful years on "the hill" in Washington, in the Justice and Interior Departments, in the office of the Chief of Staff of the Air Force at the Pentagon, in Berlin following the war, and for so many years in the VA, but I could see I had little effect. Then suddenly we heard my name:

> These are the "leaders in the Little Rock controversy" — Mrs. Joe Brewer, president of Women's Emergency Committee who has no children and who does not even live in the Little Rock school district. She is the wife of a federal employee – the Veterans Hospital facility Fort Roots. How does she justify her so active role in the school affairs of the city in which she does not even live?

Joe and I were both stiff with alertness but I had to get a copy of this speech to know what followed for Joe jumped from his chair and exclaimed, "My God, I *have* been purged!" and we heard little else the governor said.

From then on, it was a rare evening that we did not discuss Joe's demotion and the probable method of achieving it. We were particularly concerned that his record in Washington held some deleterious material. Positive that it had been placed there with malice aforethought, I was determined to extract this and destroy it if I possibly could. Joe, sensitive, deeply hurt and dejected by the troubled and disturbed atmosphere in the hospital, would have muddled through submissively, but I had to do something to expiate my guilt. I persuaded Joe to join me in writing a number of letters to try to determine what and whom we were fighting and how to proceed. I started at the top, addressing President Dwight D. Eisenhower. We wrote the Honorable Sumner G. Whittier, administrator of the VA. Joe sent a letter to Frederick J. Lawton, chairman of the Civil Service, and knowing that top officials in the government may not see their mail, to H.V. Higley, former administrator of the VA. Both of these men he had known personally. I wrote Mr. Lightsey, who had said he had a friend on the Civil Service Commission and would be glad to make contact for us if any trouble developed. No reply came from Mr. Higley, Mr. Lawton or Mr. Lightsey. Since Brooks Hays had been given a valued appointment at the White House following his defeat by Dr. Dale Alford for re-election to Congress, and since I had known Brooks most of my life, it occurred to me that he might be able to say the needed word in Washington to advise us which avenue we should take. We had one friend in the Justice Department in Washington whom we had known in our years of living in that city and who was well aware of the situation in Little Rock. He had been detailed here during the early days of the troubles in 1957 and after the WEC was organized, he wrote me congratulatory letters and even sent contributions for our work. Of all the people to whom we wrote, he and Brooks Hays probably would be the most sympathetic.

On the local scene, I made only a few contacts with friends who had close contacts with officials in high circles in the government, and although most of them wrote letters for us or made telephone calls to offices in Washington, no one found the answer. Ours was far from an isolated case of vindictive treatment; in truth we had suffered, at that point in time, far less than most who opposed the governor, for all too many were fired summarily. Harry Ashmore wrote to the Attorney General, William P. Rogers. Edwin Dunaway telephoned John Erickson, secretary to Senator William Fulbright. I wrote Bill directly to alert him to the situation but since his attitude had not been sympathetic and he had failed to acknowledge my earlier letter, I asked no favor. Mrs. Terry was almost as disturbed as was I over Joe's position. She invited a few close friends to a luncheon at her home to discuss possibilities of methods to overcome our troubles, and she made a contact for us with Mr. Nathaniel L. Harris of Boston who knew the VA administrator, Mr. Whittier, personally. Mr. Harris did all he could, promptly and wisely, but his answer was the same one we had from every approach. A few years later he was visiting in the home of the Terry's and Mrs. Terry brought him to our home for tea. Before he left, he offered an unsolicited, a telling observation: "Mr. Whittier did not understand."

Ray Huard arrived on June 3, 1959, after Joe had completed the personnel plans for the consolidation. From the first day, it was obvious what must lie ahead. Joe was assigned a room in the Little Rock VA Hospital, but he had no assistant; he was denied a secretary. He was refused a parking space, so he had to leave home much earlier in order to find room for his car and to arrive in his office on time, for a single moment of tardiness brought a nasty rebuke from Huard. "I was sent here to do a job, but I won't have to be here long. I'll get you one way or another. At one of my former assignments, I even got a good friend of the manager." Nothing Joe did was right. It was hell if you do, hell if you don't. "You are no good," Huard would shout shaking an angry finger in Joe's face. "You are not creative. You make no suggestions. You are a liar. You are a bluffer. You are a snob. If you don't please me, I'll abolish your job." And, "You can expect nothing from Central Office!"

Joe's lunch period was changed to a half hour when no others of the department were scheduled. He had no opportunity to talk with any former friends or staff assistants during the working day. Then his one outlet was nullified: Huard told him he was no longer to leave the building during his eight hour day. This included his Rotary attendance. "I've checked this out with Sterling (also a Rotarian) and he agrees you are not to attend Rotary any more." Joe asked to use his annual leave to attend this noon meeting but in vain. "Only division chiefs may participate in civic organizations. I demand the entire eight hours of your time, and at the end of each day, you are to give me a written check list on how you spend every minute of these eight hours, in complete detail."

As these cruel tactics robbed Joe of all hope, we despaired all the more to have the same bureaucratic answers to all of our pleas for help from Washington.

Twice Dr. Sterling suggested to Joe in writing that he leave the state. Twice we considered such a move as objectively as we could. Each time Joe — or was it I? — decided to try to stick it out, hoping to reach May 1961 when at the age of fifty-five he could retire on reduced annuity. He yearned to resign, that

I could see and understand, but we both faced realistically the financial problems this would entail. I kept hoping, with sublimely ridiculous optimism, that something would change, and I did not quite realize how seriously Joe's health was being affected. In August, we took as long a vacation as Joe could get approved and made our trip to Canada and California just at the time the high schools re-opened. On our return, the barrage was renewed and aggravated. Several times, through channels, Joe tried to see Dr. Sterling but Huard maneuvered to prevent this. We had information that copies of our letters to Washington and of the answers had been sent to Dr. Sterling and had been read by Mr. Huard. This did not help. Huard's next tactic was to assert that he could not go ahead with Joe's job sheet, that Joe had to prove himself. The timely filing of this information and evaluation was important under personnel regulations and custom, so Joe filed the job sheet himself. Huard was furious and increasingly sadistic.

Finally on the first day of December, Joe told Huard bluntly that with or without his approval, he was going to seek an appointment with Dr. Sterling. "You are not to see Sterling until my plans are completed," Huard admonished. With the months of daily pressure, Joe was breaking visibly. I told him that his health came first and I would rather he would resign than take punishment which might make him an invalid. I meant that, of course, but when he called me at the WEC office and told me he had taken all he could, that under the degrading badgering he had consented to write a letter asking for the abolishment of his job, I urged him to put nothing in writing.

Without Joe's knowledge, I immediately called Senator Fulbright's office. Surely this turn of events would bring action. Over the weekend I persuaded Joe not to file the desired letter with Huard. I acknowledged that I had renewed contact with Washington. Completely exhausted, Joe appeared displeased but eventually agreed, "All right, I'll try to take it a little longer. At least we will have done all we can."

When Joe told Huard he had decided not to sign the letter, that such a request on his part would be questionable if not actually illegal, Huard exclaimed, "But I've already told the manager you would. Now how can I explain this to him?"

After some maddening delays, I had a long talk with Senator Fulbright's secretary; he asked me to talk with Mr. Monk, the chief of personnel in the VA Washington Office. Going to a pay phone in a rural area, I did my best to convince Mr. Monk of the seriousness of our situation. He promised he would send an investigator, and despite the fact that we learned he also called Sterling and Huard, our hopes rose. We spent hours compiling a list of people to whom we hoped the investigator would talk. Few of these, alas, were employed by the VA for we dared not involve anyone who did not volunteer, knowing full well that this would doubtless seal their doom. On Tuesday, December 15th, Joe telephoned me that Mr. Kenneth E. Everett, special investigator from the

VA Investigation Service of Central Office, had arrived and wished to talk with us in our home. We found him a very pleasant man whom we might have enjoyed knowing under other circumstances. He explained that Joe's testimony and that of others he might interview would be taped but that he would like me to file a sworn statement with him. I spent a full day and a half writing and typing this statement and arranging accompanying exhibits, and we delivered this to Mr. Everett in his room at the Hotel Sam Peck as we said good-bye to him on Thursday afternoon, December 17th.

Checking with our brave friends who had offered to testify, we found that Mr. Everett had contacted very few of them. Joe's former assistant was one: our good friend, Jim O'Donnell, and he was to suffer the same torment and eventual retirement. Mr. Everett's stay was brief and he mentioned only one of our kind friends to us: Mrs. Terry for whose personality and character he had high compliments. He expressed, most agreeably, pleasure in knowing us. And that was all we gained from this episode; the pressures only increased.

Over Huard's protest, Joe, with difficulty and delay, at long last took his story to Dr. Sterling. Both the manager and Mr. Wilbur heard him through without a query or a comment. At the end, Mr. Wilbur uttered not a sound, made not a move; Dr. Sterling dismissed Joe with a curt, "I assumed you must have a side."

On March 14, 1960, R.G. Huard gave notice in writing to Joe that he would be affected by a reduction in force in the personnel office. This was the equivalent of the abolishment of his job. Huard instructed him that he must decide within five days whether he would take a reassignment out of the state — or just get out. At this juncture, both Joe's private physician and a neurologist at the VA Hospital in North Little Rock insisted that Joe not go back to his office, advising that he could not take any more of the interminable strain without seriously endangering his health. These doctors signed papers for him to apply for a disability retirement on the grounds of acute depression and anxiety as a result of nervous reaction. On May 2nd, this application was medically approved and on May 16th (what a birthday gift!) his disability retirement was approved. Huard immediately canceled the reduction in force notices issued to Joe on March 14, 1960 and April 6, 1960; Joe came home a free man. His joyous relief was almost more than I could bear to watch — or was it the realization that we had lost so devastatingly?

Throughout these months, we had constant reports of unrest and fear in both the Little Rock and the North Little Rock VA hospitals. Many of the employees, knowing of our plight, told us apologetically, "I've learned I have to keep my mouth shut."

One day a young business man came up to me on the street and said, "I hope Dale Alford suffers some day." And why Dale Alford? I suppose his statement about us in his book, his violently segregationists views and his appointment to the Civil Service Committee of the House of Representatives in

Washington spread the suspicion that he had a major role in Joe's retirement.

We wondered ourselves, so a small event took on significance. At the airport one day in the fall of 1960, having said farewell to an aunt, retracing our steps throughout the terminal, we were suddenly aware of Dale Alford watching us with a broad, smugly malicious grin. A cousin, preceding me, gestured, "Did you see Dr. Alford?" And then, startled, "Why, he is grinning at *you!*" It was quite obvious that he was, and I wondered again about the possibility of his major role in our personal defeat.

We didn't know, of course, and could only guess the source of our traumatic year and the methods which had been used. We did know that Dr. Sterling had a son working for the state. It seemed more than interesting that the *Arkansas Recorder* (a Faubus publication) ran a large picture of Phil Sterling with a complimentary story on his "fascinating" activities in the state Geological and Conservation Department. It was more than a year later that a friend whom we trusted implicitly told Joe of a meeting early in 1959 at which Governor Faubus told Dr. Sterling to "get rid of Joe Brewer or else." Still we had no proof.

Although I was seeing many people daily, spending long hours at the office, this was a lonely time for us. Joe became understandably anti-social, trusting almost no man, and we were both too enervated to seek society. Fearful that our distress might frighten members of the WEC and weaken the committee, I told only a few about Joe's forced retirement. Closest friends were kind but they realized that Joe needed peace and quiet as the antidote to his days of torture.

1960 was not without encouragement and happiness. On a Saturday in early November, Joe came in from the yard to find me bathed in "sweet tears."

"My God,' he shouted in justifiable alarm, "What has happened now?" My voice deserting me, I gave him the letter which had just come from Thomas C. Mendenhall, President of Smith College. It read in part:

> Dear Mrs. Brewer:
>
> It gives me great pleasure to inform you that the Smith College Board of Trustees has voted to give you an honorary degree next June.

I drove myself to hold the WEC together as best I could through that politically imbued year of 1960, working early and late, five and sometimes seven days a week. This, too, must have been anguish for Joe, but he did not ask me to quit. The calm, completely peaceful opening of the schools on September 6, 1960, with seven Negroes enrolled at Central High School and five at Hall High confirmed my decision to resign as chairman of the Women's Emergency Committee. Over many flattering protests I was adamant in my resolve to step down. I informed the executive committee early in the fall that I would like to be relieved by November, telling them only that Joe now needed me more than they did. I agreed to stay on as a member of the Executive Board.

From left: Vivion Brewer, founder and first Chair;
Adolphine Terry, founder; Pat House, second and last Chair.

There developed a difficult quest for a new slate of officers. After a soul-searching conference with Mrs. Terry and myself, Pat (Mrs. Byron, Jr.) House, a tireless worker notwithstanding four children ages two to eight years, agreed to serve as chairman. Jo Jackson who had spoken so ably at the rally for the STOP organization, promised to be an active vice-chairman.

When I phoned Jo about this office, she gave me a new view of myself. "Who will be the chairman?" she asked.

"Pat House," I told her.

"Oh," she demurred, "I thought she was already chairman."

Meekly I explained that I had been chairman but was resigning.

"Oh," she said again, "I thought you were like Mrs. Terry — just there!"

I could not claim to be like Mrs. Terry — but I was there!

When Pat House knew she was to assume the leadership of the WEC, she asked me for suggestions for her acceptance speech. Aware of continuing problems, I gave her these notes:

> Election of city directors is of vital concern to us, since we have learned in the past two years what an important part the City Board of Directors plays in helping solve the problems surrounding the public school system.

277

Terms of two members of the School Board (Matson and McDonald) expire this year. Neither has yet announced whether he will seek re-election in December. It is of paramount interest to us that we have a strong Board, dedicated to the preservation and improvement of our public schools.

In January we will again have the legislature with us. We should give thought to legislation which will protect and improve our schools. We should keep close contact with the Pulaski County representatives, and let us be cheered that we have the promise of several of these men that they not only will listen to us but actually will seek our opinions.

Urge everyone to keep in close touch with our activities. Our office is open daily from 10 until 3 Monday trough Friday. Our telephone is listed in the name of the WEC. If we do not get news letters to you (and remember it is a real expense to produce and mail these news sheets) call the office with questions, with suggestions, with criticisms. Let us know you are interested. YOU are our strength. Without your co-operation and enthusiasm, we can hope to do little. And how much there is yet to do!

The *Arkansas Gazette* printed a gratifying editorial in the fall of 1961:

Bless the Ladies

The fact that Little Rock now has a permanent Women's Emergency Committee for Public Schools does not make the travail of the last few years worth-while. Nothing could. But the existence of this organization, which celebrated its third anniversary last Tuesday, is one of the principal means by which we can try at least to rationalize some purifying and strengthening values out of that community-wide submission to the Bessemer process.

Looking back now, it is still faintly terrifying to speculate on what Little Rock would have done without that first small gathering together of women who were determined that the schools would be saved, and who, by the strength of their example, did more than any other group to create the wave of public opinion that finally saw to it that the schools WERE saved.

"To the Ladies, God bless 'em."

The Ladies carried on until November of 1963, but the organization was doomed to splinter. Minus a unifying goal and divided in support of candidates for the School Board and for other positions, the membership gradually lessened and weakened. The women, now civically aware, undertook more specific activities: in the League of Women Voters; in the American Association of University Women; in the Urban League; in the Arkansas Council on Human Relations (I was to serve as chairman of this organization in ensuing years); in the National Conference of Christians and Jews; in the Catholic Inter-racial Council; in PTAs; in churches; in politics; in education. In all facets of human relations and the fight for the good life in our community, wherever action was indicated, some of the WEC members were *there*. Our committee had brought its women to an alert realization of problems, had taught them the need for and the value of their concern. Our city and our state are the richer for it. So, when on November 2nd, 1963, the WEC voted itself out of existence, there were public accolades. One of our favorites was an editorial in the *Pine Bluff Commercial* of November 25th.

Our favorite quote from Governor Faubus, now in his fifth term, was elicited when he was asked his attitude toward the demise of his relentless antagonist. He opined that the members of the WEC probably would "try to infiltrate other organizations. It might have been better to have them all in one group."

Well, who were the members? Early in 1960, Anne Helvenston brought to the Executive Board a suggestion for another survey, this time of ourselves. Several objectives motivated the idea:

    a) to learn, for publicity uses, the characteristics of personal history and opinion of the membership;

Pine Bluff Commercial, November 25, 1963:

TAPS

If the men of Arkansas had more self respect, they would bow their heads at the demise of the Women's Emergency Committee of Little Rock.

But if the men of Arkansas had more self respect, the Women's Emergency Committee would never have had to come into existence in the first place. It was a desperation organization by a handful of ladies who knew not what they should do about it but who were dead certain that the state of Arkansas should not be turned over to racists and allied wreckers.

The ladies found their footing almost as soon as they had voted in a chairman, and have seldom lost it since. It seems little short of incredible, only five years after the fact, that they were from their beginning almost all of the organized opposition to efforts by Orval E. Faubus to abandon the public schools. It is a measure of how far we have come — often being dragged kicking and screaming by the ladies of the committee — that a gubernatorial candidate who today advocated school closure as an "answer" to desegregation would be dismissed as charlatan or an unusually primitive boob. The ladies now disband, and thus signal the end of an era in which they were one of the few things to be remembered with pride – an era which might have been a much larger and more enduring disaster (not that it wasn't large enough, and didn't endure long enough), had the Women's Emergency Committee not made its appearance. In essence, the committee took the lead after this state's so-called leadership had either gone over to the other side of retrogression and racism or had fled through the nearest available exit. The ladies now pass the seals of leadership back to their conventional custodians. These custodians ought to be on notice, however, that the committee could be put together again in an afternoon, and doubtless will be should the need arise.

b) to use the same information to guide the board in approaching its own membership for co-operation, and in educating it;

c) to educate the membership to the fact that some school problems remain to be solved;

d) to discover something about the place of the group in the social structure of the whole community.

Carefully, a questionnaire was prepared, covering three pages. This was mailed under date of March 23, 1960 to 1371 members of the WEC residing in the Little Rock — North Little Rock area and to a half dozen or so particularly active members who had moved away in the previous three weeks. "We have been called old, young, frustrated and a few other things," I wrote. "Well, are we?" In block letters each member was instructed: "DO NOT SIGN ANY PAGE" and I assured each one that the answers would be absolutely anonymous.

Over half of the survey forms, 720, were returned, one of which was blank: a man? The forms were numbered as they were received in the office. Twenty-five or more committee members helped in tabulating the results, working an estimated 2,000 hours voluntarily to record several thousand items of data.

We heard little complaint of the survey. However, there were a few objections to the question of income. A few objected to queries on church affiliation. One or two members said they falsified a few replies to insure that they would not be recognized. Some left the question on integration blank while they filled in the personal history information.

On June 26, 1960, we gave the press a preliminary report of our statistics, promising that more would come later:

In age, 42% of us were 37 to 50; 25% were 26 to 36 and 17% were 51 to 60; 2% were under 26; 14% over 61.

80% were married, 9% were single; the rest separated, divorced or widowed.

61% had lived in Little Rock or Arkansas 20 or more years; 9% in the south for that time.

Home owners constituted 73%, and 44% of them had family incomes of $8,500 to $15,000; 35% had under $8,500 and 22% over $15,000.

Most were church members and 65% had done volunteer work for the committee.

The husbands of 85% were privately employed; 7% worked for the federal government; 6% for the state; 1% for local governments. 13% were wives of doctors.

41% of the wives and 25% of their husbands had some college education. 20% of the members and 24% of their husbands had 4 years of college; 21% of the women and 39% of their husbands had more than 4 years of college.

91% of the respondents planned their future in Arkansas. 9% expected to leave the state. Of that 9%, 31% of the women and 50% of their husbands had more than four years of college.

38% had 2 children; 26% had 3; 20% had only one. 11% had 4 children; 3% had 5; 1% had 6; 0.16% each had 7 and 8. The total was 1,446 children with 50% in public schools, 10% in college; 19% past college age. 10% were due to attend the closed high schools in 1958–1959. 21% were pre-school children.

82% of the women had worked before marriage, in occupations ranging from modeling to banking. 23% of the sample still worked, full or part time.

Studying the results of the survey, I was disturbed by some of the answers which we were careful not to divulge:

How many of your close neighbors share your views on the school crisis?

None	1 or 2	Some	Most	No answer	# answering
30	130	241	190	129	591

Percentile responses

None	1 or 2	Some	Most	No answer	# answering
5%	22%	41%	32%	18%	82%

Were your personal relations with any neighbors or friends changed by the school crisis?

Yes	208	33%
No	428	67%
# ans.	628	87%
Omit	92	13%

Does your husband in general share your attitude on the school crisis? Do your parents?

Husband and parents agree on schools (of 400 answering):

Yes	235
No	1

Husband and parents disagree

Husband, yes; parents, no	140	35%
Reverse	24	6%

Indeed, I have never been sure that, strive as we did to protect our membership, some subsequent estrangements of friends and family, and even divorces, may not have stemmed from devotion to our program.

There were, on the other hand, answers which interested and pleased me, and these we publicized in September:

Do you believe that desegregation will permanently damage public education?

% answering	Yes	No	Don't Know
92	15	82	3

If Little Rock public eating places were opened to Negro customers, would you approve, disapprove, wouldn't care?

% answering	% Approve	% Disapprove	% Wouldn't Care
91	37	21	42

I did not say so then but I suspected that the answers in the fall of 1959 would have been much less liberal. We had all come a long way together.

It was our intention to issue an analysis of the entire survey. We believed that there was in it important infor-mation for development of woman power, of political activism, of social change. Unfortunately, with all there was to do that summer of 1960, this study was temporarily shelved, and when Grace Malakoff, who was qualified to undertake this project, moved to Washington, D.C., the boxes of survey sheets went with her. At last report, they had an honored place in the corner of her living room awaiting those elusive spare hours even as this documentary has awaited mine.

Perhaps, as an addendum, I can summarize the whole story of the Women's Emergency Committee by quoting once more from the *Arkansas Gazette*. On November 5, 1963, this excellent and long suffering newspaper editorialized:

The WEC Retires Its Battle-honored Flag

The Women's Emergency Committee was born by parthenogenesis for a purpose that was widely thought of as heresy at the time (1958). It now has committed the double heresy of decreeing its own dissolution, once that founding purpose was accomplished and the public schools restored to some-thing resembling their former standing as one of the first articles of our democratic faith.

There probably is nothing wrong with the country that could not be materially alleviated by dissolving all the organizations that have outlived the purpose of their founding – if, indeed, they ever had any. The WEC,

---

however, never belonged to that company, nor does it belong now in that infinitesimal company of organizations that vote themselves out of business at some point short of the funeral of the last eligible member. Indeed, if the rest of us defer to the members' own good judgment now, and let them get by with it, it is only because we have had so many occasions to respect that judgment through the five years of the WEC's existence.

Perhaps the most common misconception surrounding the group during those years was that it was concerned only with the preservation of the Little Rock public school system. In the nature of things, that had to be the primary concern of the wives and mothers of the WEC, but it was never their sole concern. In quite a real sense, the WEC's many battles were but an extension of battles fought by the founders of the American system of free public education in every part of the country in the very beginning. The embattled ladies of Little Rock were fighting for the continuance of the public school concept in Little Rock, in Arkansas, in the South and in the country as a whole. There are children now in school in cities where no one has ever heard of the Women's Emergency Committee of Little Rock who quite possibly would not be there if the WEC had not existed in the time and place that it did. There are other cities where local parent and professional groups are quite aware of the debt they owe to Little Rock's and WEC's example, for the Arkansas organization's techniques of direct political action came to be widely copied at other critical points in the Southern school crisis.

Little Rock was where the first shock of major battle was felt, but it was also the place where the tide first began to turn. Those of us who shared the same command post under fire have never doubted that the outcome would have been somewhat different, had it not been for the selfless volunteers of the Women's Emergency Committee.

APPENDIXES

Appendix 1

A Brief Biography of

Adolphine Fletcher Terry

Adolphine Fletcher Terry (Mrs. David D. Terry, Sr.) is a member of a distinguished Arkansas family. Her father, Colonel John G. Fletcher, was an officer in the Confederate Army, the first Democratic sheriff of Pulaski County after Reconstruction days, "a member of a great many financial institutions in Little Rock — ever ready to lend a helping hand to any public enterprise" (*Arkansas Case Democrat, 1906*) and the mayor of Little Rock from 1875 to 1881. Her brother, John Gould Fletcher, the eminent poet, was a recipient of a Pulitzer prize. Since her early childhood, she with her family has lived in the ante-bellum mansion at 411 East Seventh Street in Little Rock, which had been built in 1840 by a "ranking Confederate, Albert Pike." This home she opens to the public two afternoons each week and makes available to countless organizations and individuals for meetings, teas, receptions. Many a significant movement for the public welfare has started at a small luncheon around her oval dining table. The days of usefulness for this historic landmark are unnumbered, for it has been deeded by Mrs. Terry and her sister, Mrs. Mary Fletcher Drennan of Baltimore, Maryland, to the City of Little Rock to be administered at the end of their lives by the Arkansas Arts Center Board of Trustees.* Living with her there now are

---

* The house is now the Decorative Arts Museum and displays commemorative plaques honoring the members of the WEC.

289

her two daughters, Sally Terry Plummer and Mary Fletcher Terry, and she is the mother of William L. Terry of Little Rock, Joseph Terry of Memphis, Tennessee and the late Colonel David D. Terry, Jr. Her husband, David D. Terry Sr., who died October 5, 1963, had a long and active life also, the significance of which is memorialized by the David D. Terry Elementary School in Little Rock and the David D. Terry Dam on the Arkansas River, the navigability of which was one of his dreams. It was during the years 1933 to 1942 when Dave Terry was Representative from the Fifth District in Arkansas in the United States Congress that Adolphine made an unforgettable impression on me by phoning now and then to ask not "What are you *doing* these days?" but "What are you *thinking* about now?" To list her contributions would fill a tome, but at least a few must be noted. Her fight for better education has become a legend. "We here in Arkansas are most hospitable, the kindest, the most generous people on earth, but we have to admit it," she theorized when a few screaming men and women made her beloved city internationally infamous in 1957, "we are just plain ignorant." As early as 1908, with Miss Blanche Martin, she worked to promote school consolidation and to get county school superintendents in each county. She organized the first School Improvement Association which was the infant PTA in Arkansas. She started the State Library Board. She served on the Board of the Little Rock Public Library for 35 years. In 1961, her alma mater, Vassar College, celebrating its 100th anniversary, selected her as one of its one hundred most distinguished graduates. She organized the Pulaski County Juvenile Court in 1910, the first juvenile court in the state. She has left her mark on almost every charitable organization and on all the public welfare agencies. She helped establish the Pulaski County TB Association and served on its board. She served on the boards of the Family Service Agency and the Salvation Army. It was she who made the suggestion that a Community Chest be formed in Little Rock. She was the United Nations Chairman of the Federation of Women's Clubs and took a group of women to visit the United Nations. She served as a delegate to the Democratic Convention during the administration of Franklin D. Roosevelt and, during one of his campaigns, toured Nebraska speaking for him. She marched down Main Street in the days of the suffragettes carrying a banner demanding equal rights for women. "And we still haven't got them," she quips. She has had a life-long interest in cultural and religious affairs. She initiated the Arkansas State Festival of Arts and served for two years as its chairman. She has been a staunch member of the Christ Episcopal Church, serving on the Parish Council and teaching Sunday School. She has served on the boards of the Civic Music Association and the State Opera Association and when no one else would volunteer she headed a committee to raise funds for the University of Arkansas' Schola Cantorum so they might return to Europe. The help she has given to the poor and needy, the young and the old, is beyond anyone's knowledge. I sat with her in her den one day when a young man from Tanzania told us in faltering English that he had come all the way to the end of his four years at Philander Smith College and now could not graduate for the lack of $35.00. "That is ridiculous," Mrs. Terry said as she whipped out her check book and hastily wrote out a check for him. Innumerable times, I have answered a knock at her door to be confronted by a pleading haggard face and an often soiled out-stretched hand. "Oh, look in my purse, please, and give him a quarter or fifty cents," she would say. "I cannot turn anyone down completely. Who knows?" Mrs. Terry can pin-point her farewell to prejudice. It was in her first year at Vassar when a college friend, Lucy Burns of New York, "older and smarter than I," and a number of classmates were sitting talking one night that the question of the Negro came up. Without thinking Adolphine blandly made a statement which she had heard all her life: "If a Negro assaults a white woman, he should be lynched as quickly as possible." Lucy recoiled in horror and demanded "In order to wreak vengeance on one poor wretch, would you destroy the very foundation of law and order in your community?" Adolphine sat very still pondering this question. "And of course I knew she was right."

Appendix 2

A Brief Biography of

Velma Wood Powell

The young woman who wrote the letter to Mrs. Terry is also an Arkansan. "My great, great grandparents settled in southern Arkansas," Velma Wood related, "in a small community which grew into the town of Monticello." Her birthplace now has a population of about 4500. It is situated only 30 miles from the Louisiana line and perhaps 20 miles from the Mississippi River. "When my mother and father married," she continued, "the story was told that they made everybody on the north side and the south side of Monticello relative." This made for a happy childhood being "kin to" almost everyone in town, and looking upon any person whose family had not lived in the village at least 50 years as a "newcomer."

"When I was 18," Velma remembers, "the furtherst north I had been was Springfield, Missouri, the furtherst east, Memphis, Tennessee, but I had visited many relatives in Louisiana and Mississippi all my life." Monticello had no Unitarian Church, no Catholic Church, no Jewish Temple, no Greek Church, in short "no so-called foreign element in the sense of different ideas." There was a small state college, Arkansas Agricultural and Mechanical College, located there and this Velma attended, but after she acquired her B.A. in English and History, she wanted a business course. Her mother wrote to Mrs. Terry in Little Rock to ask if she knew of a place her sheltered daughter could live while she attended Draughan's Business College. Mrs. Terry with her generous spirit answered at once: "We have plenty of room. Let her come live with us." So Velma came to be one of the Terry family and her horizons suddenly broadened.

Of a naturally inquisitive nature, she read widely on many subjects. She liked people, enjoyed long discussions and she made many friends among both white citizens and Negroes. "If you want to know what the southern Negro thinks," she once said, "do not accept someone else's idea. Go to the source, and do not expect one or two to give you the answer."

Moving to Little Rock in 1946, she soon felt it was home. She met her future husband at a Christmas dance that first year, on a blind date, and they were married in June of 1947. J.O. (Jay) Powell was attending Little Rock Junior College then but entered Hendrix College in Conway that fall, graduating in May of 1949 with honors and the McCuiston Prize in English. During these years Velma had her first job as secretary to Mrs. Alice H. Funston, Director of the Arkansas American Legion Child Welfare program, but in June, she and Jay moved to Philadelphia where Jay received his M.A. in 1950. There Velma worked as secretary to the medical director of J.B. Lippincott, Publishers. Returning to Little Rock in 1951 and buying a home, Jay began to teach English and German at Central high School and in 1955 became vice-principal for boys. Meanwhile Velma was the executive director of the Ouachita Area Girl Scout Council for two years. From this job, she moved first to the Arkansas Council on Human Relations (A.C.H.R.) until its funds ran low; then for a year and a half to the Pulaski County Red Cross as a social case-worker; ultimately back to A.C.H.R. in the fall of 1958. During much of this time she was a board member of the Little Rock League of Women Voters and also the State League; she worked with the Little Rock Community Chest, serving as a member of its budget committee; she joined Adult Education groups; she was active in the Youth Co-ordinating Council.

Although Velma lived the year with the Terrys and is related to close friends of ours in Little Rock, our paths did not cross until the winter of 1957. Our first meeting was a brief one at the home of her cousins. Perhaps because their social philosophy is so diametrically opposed to Velma's and mine, Velma and I quickly recognized each other as cohorts. It was she who told me some of the lurid tales of the experiences of the young Negroes at Central High that bitter year of 1957–58 and of the reactions of the teachers and of the administrative staff.

In the spring of 1958 she served on Joe's committee for arrangements for the Pulitzer prize dinner for the *Arkansas Gazette.* These two contacts prompted her suggestion that I might chair the group which became the Women's Emergency Committee that fall.

Appendix 3

Half Page Advertisement in a
Little Rock Newspaper, Sept. 1958

DO WE WANT THIS KIND OF
PUBLIC SCHOOLS IN ARKANSAS?

Here is part of the record of the Integrated Public Schools in Washington, D.C., our nation's capital, covering the seven months period from September 1957 through April 1958. Source of information is report to Commissioner's Youth Council, District of Columbia by Dr. John R. Pate, chief of D.C. Disease Control Bureau.

Total pregnancies reported	185
Among Negro girls	169
Among white girls	16

At age of 12: 5 girls, all Negro
At age of 13: 22 girls, 20 Negro, 2 white
At age of 14: 81 girls, 74 Negro, 7 white
At age of 15: 77 girls, 70 Negro, 7 white

Venereal Disease Increase

A report on venereal diseases for the 12 months ending June 30, 1958 reveals the following:

Total cases: 896   Whites: 13 (boys: 13   girls: 5)
Among Negroes: 883 (boys: 258   girls: 625)

To those people in Arkansas who think they could accept integrated schools, we urge that you study the above facts. Is this the kind of schools you want your children to attend?

CAPITAL CITIZENS COUNCIL
Malcolm Taylor, President

Appendix 4

First Published Newsletter

June 8, 1959 . . .Women's Emergency Committee, Little Rock, Ark., No 1

Rumors drift in that the recall election celebration left us in a vacuum. Nothing could be more untrue! We all needed a short respite, but now we must capitalize on our recent victory with an even more determined voice and an expanded program. Letters indicate that many recognize and value the work we have done and the big part we played in the dramatic success of STOP.

It seemed practical to suspend our monthly meetings for the summer, but our executive committee will continue to meet each Wednesday morning.

We urge you to phone ideas and suggestions to any one of this committee.

Most of you know our office is in a new location but our telephone is the same. Since vacations and the summer home duties of mothers will interrupt our schedules,

We need volunteers for various phases of our activities, from staffing the office to addressing envelopes.

<u>PLEASE CALL IN IF YOU CAN GIVE ANY TIME AT ALL,</u>

<u>NOW OR LATER.</u>

We wish to make one correction of a statement you may have heard. Further research on Act 248 has revealed great confusion in the date of the next school board election; several conflicting dates, from September to December, appear in the title, the body of the act and the amendments to it. Probably an opinion of the Attorney General will be needed to determine the valid date, but it would appear that the next school board election may be held either on the first Tuesday in December as shown in the enactment clause, or the first Saturday in December as decreed by the old law. A bulletin on this will be issued later.

In order to vote in this election or any other between October 2, 1959, and October 1, 1960, inclusive, you must have purchased the 1959 poll tax now available. (Remember the 1958 poll tax receipt enabled you to vote in the recall election but expires October 1, 1959. We were dismayed to find many of our group were not in the 1958 poll tax listings.) If you have not already done so, go out today and buy your 1959 poll tax before you forget it!!!

Besides open schools in Little Rock this September, we have another goal of vital importance. In the general election of November 1960, we vote on a constitutional amendment which could mean the complete destruction of our public school system. This threat must be fought <u>beginning now</u> and not only in Little Rock but all over the state.

Can you give us names of potential allies in any area in Arkansas?

Or suggest sources of additional lists? There are other ways you can help:

<u>Get new members</u>! A sudden increase will be an effective answer to the public attack on our committee.

<u>Write Letters</u> to the Editors of the papers—any place in the state—but particularly to the *Arkansas Democrat* in support of public schools.

<u>Participate in Party Line</u>. Try to call in statements in support of public education to Party Line on KLRA, between 7 and 10 p.m., Monday through Saturday.

<u>Talk</u> of our Committee and its work FOR EDUCATION.

If you can afford to repeat or increase your donation to our Committee, <u>we'll welcome financial support </u>of our enlarged program.

One thing more: We've often wondered how many women would now consent to the public use of their names in support of public schools. WOULD YOU?

If you would, please call us and say so.

We'll be talking to you again soon.
<u>We count on your talking to us NOW</u>!

Appendix 5

Questions Most Frequently Asked by Parents

Summer 1959 for information of W.E.C. members:

How can we be sure there will be no violence in the schools?

What measures are being taken to insure safety?

Will Federal Marshalls supplement the City Police?

Should private citizens supplement the police? Should it be parents? Should it be W.E.C. members?

What happened to the libel suit against McKinley and Moser?

What happened to the Stephens-Laster suit?

What happened to the case regarding the circular during the recall election?

What about the appeal of Acts 4 and 5 by the Governor? Will this delay school opening? What if a stay is granted? How long will the opening be delayed?

Where can you find exactly the specifics of the Little Rock plan of integration as approved by the Court?

Will East Side Junior High be integrated this year?

When will East Side Junior High be integrated? Will there be over 60% Negroes in East Side Junior High when it is integrated?

Will the standard of education in the Little Rock schools be maintained if Negroes are enrolled in the white schools?

Will there be "mixing" in school social activities?

Will there be "mixed" participation in school sports?

How can you tell your child to be friendly with the Negroes without becoming too friendly?

What will happen if a Negro child refuses to follow white student leadership?

Will gangs be allowed to form on each side?

How will pressure from the extremists prevent the Negro child from being resentful?

What about disciplinary problems?

Will Negroes teach my children?

Is there anything in any regulation which would prevent children living in the Hall High District being sent to Horace Mann under the pupil placement plan?

These Are Questions Most Commonly Asked

with answers from action patterns in school desegregation:

What about Negro "cultural" differences? "Certainly there are cultural differences within the white race that a good teacher has had to plan for. Therefore, if a teacher knows how to take care of these problems, he or she should be able to do so in a Negro-white situation."

What about "special problems?"

"There is a tendency to assign racial significance to problems which are simply problems. This is to be expected, at least until people stop talking so much about race and integration and start talking about students and education."

Would you want a Negro to marry your daughter? "This question is countered that fear of intermarriage results from desegregation with statistics showing that in northern parts of the United States where there has been no segregation, intermarriage is a rare thing indeed."

Are measles caught from Negroes more severe? "Reputable medical authorities say no."

Isn't there a high rate of disease among Negro Children, and won't my children contract venereal and other diseases from them by using the same toilets, drinking fountains, and the cafeteria? "The problem is not big and here is how we know: We tested 12,000 children four years ago, and there were only eight infectious cases in the 12,000." (In talking with the Arkansas Public Health Department it was stated that the incidence of venereal disease among children below nineteen was so low that no statistics were kept. Venereal disease is not easily communicable except through intercourse—cannot be caught through drinking fountains, and the use of the same toilets and cafeterias.)

Is there more sexual immorality in the Negro school than the white? "Of which we have knowledge, there are more pregnancies in the Negro high schools."

What will be done about diseased Negro children in school? "In schools we shall maintain normal health and sanitation standards and exclude any pupil suffering from infectious or contagious diseases."

Is there an inherent race difference in intelligence? "There is no scientific evidence that inherent intelligence is higher or lower in any group of people, according to one reliable source."

Can great numbers of children with low test scores such as Negroes be brought to a higher level of achievement through increased opportunities? "All evidence points to a rise in achievement as measured by standard tests when individual opportunities and incentives to learn are improved in the home, school, or the community generally, according to the same source."

Appendix 6

Integration Recommendations

Recognizing the school year of 1959-60 must have a different approach to smooth operation, we offer the following suggestions gathered from anonymous interviews with teachers and parents connected with Central High. Most of the recommendations are particularly applicable to Central High but many are appropriate for one or more of the other schools:

1. It is suggested that definite efforts be made to prepare students, parents and teachers to adjust to a desegregated school system. A study of the Louisville and St. Louis plans would be valuable.

2. If the members of the School Board have not already done so, it is suggested that they go in a conducted tour of the four high schools—with special attention to Central because of the problems involved in maintaining discipline in a plant of that size.

3. It is recommended that an inter-communication system be installed in Central High to assist in alleviating disciplinary problems, if not in every classroom, at least spaced on each floor.

4. A suggestion has been made that, since there will be many children of segregationists in Central High, authority for disciplinary functions be shifted to a special department.

5. It is recommended that the School Board draw up a strong policy on discipline immediately and send it to the administrators designated to implement the policy. Also that this policy be made public in order to reassure parents, students and the entire community.

6. It is suggested that there be detailed rules of conduct

and behavior drawn up by the administrators with the aid of the student council. These rules should be strictly enforced.

a. If there are racial incidents, written summaries should be sent to the superintendent on the day they occur.

b. Case histories of known repeaters should be reviewed and these students allowed to return to classes with the recommendation that after a third offense, the student be suspended.

c. Students leaders should be used in every way possible within the school to help keep order and prevent vandalism.

7. Particular emphasis should be placed on assigning a committee or squad to specific posts in halls and cafeteria during class exchanges, and lunch periods; also at building entrances and exits and at Campus Inn during school hours, and on the grounds perhaps a half hour before the building opens and after it closes. The purpose of this committee would be to detect and prevent a) harassment of pupils, b) presence of unauthorized persons, c) property damage to the school plan. (Preventable vandalism cost the taxpayers hundreds of dollars during the 1957-58 year at Central.)

8. In the past, students have occupied any lockers they chose. It is suggested that all lockers be assigned, and lock combinations be kept in the main office. Whenever feasible, it is recommended that teachers assign lockers in blocks outside their classrooms.

9. It is suggested that

a. Buildings open at 8:15

b. Teachers be in their classrooms by 8:15

c. There be minimum loitering in the corridors and on the grounds

d. Advance permission be required for early entrance to school or remaining after school hours.

e. Issuance of hall passes be held to a minimum.

Appendix 7

WEC Members Working on
The Little Rock Report

The Interviewers

Mrs. Albert Ahrens
Mrs. L. Prentice Booe
Mrs. Calvin Dillaha
Mrs. Casper Dum
Mrs. S.J. Fileds
Mrs. Charles Henry
Mrs. Byron House, Jr.
Mrs. James L. Jackson
Mrs. Payton Kolb
Mrs. Frank Lambright
Mrs. Lewis M.K. Long
Mrs. Frank McGehee
Mrs. Woodbridge Morris
Mrs. Tom Norman
Mrs. Herbert Storthz
Mrs. Gordon N. Wilson
Mrs. James Youngdahl

The Advisory Board

Mrs. Joe R. Brewer
Mrs. D.D. Terry
Mrs. Woodbridge Morris
Miss Ada May Smith
Mrs. John M. Samuel
Mrs. Harry Ashmore
Miss Parma Basham
Mrs. W.C. Johnston
Mrs. Edward Lester
Mrs. Robert Shults
Mrs. W.H. Thompson
Mrs. E. Grainger Williams

Appendix 8

Summary of Amendment 52

SAVE OUR PUBLIC SCHOOLS
VOTE AGAINST AMENDMENT #52

WHAT 52 PROPOSES TO DO!

Section I: Abolishes our present constitutional guarantee of free schools.

Section III: Instead of guaranteeing public schools for all Arkansas children, allows each school district to decide between public schools and a student financial aid program.

Section VI: Destroys the electors' control of the rate of tax levy. If any proposed change in the rate (up or down) fails, the rate is arbitrarily set at 30 mills or the present rate whichever is lower.

Section VII: Restricts credit of school districts. They could no longer secure mortgages on real property. Rates of interest would doubtless rise.

Section VIII: If a school district votes to distribute funds to its pupils, it must first pay all contractual obligations, e.g., insurance, bonds, teacher contracts, maintenance. The remaining funds would then be equally distributed among all the pupils in the district, whether enrolled in public, private or parochial schools. Furthermore, once a district votes a preference for student aid, it can not reconsider legally for at least a year.

Section IX: Changes the way constitutional amendments relating to schools may be made. A special election to amend the constitution could be called on thirty (30) days notice (instead of the waiting period now required) giving the voters no time to study or even learn of the issues involved.

Section XI: Repeals all reference to public education now in our constitution. Our guarantee of free public education is nullified.

ASK YOURSELF THESE QUESTIONS!

What is the future of your children without public education? What kind of an education would a pro-rata share in available funds buy? Can you afford a private school?

What kind of schools would a 30 mill tax rate provide? (The current Little Rock rate is 40 mills, the Pulaski County (Rural) rate is 45 mills.)

What would happen to the school buildings? How would improvements and expansion be obtained?

What would happen to your teachers? Could you find suitable educational facilities for your children? Would adjoining districts accept larger enrollments, and if they did, what would be the cost in tuition, transportation, efficiency and home tensions? Would many children choose no school at all? Might you be paying taxes to support closed schools?

Would families move away to states having good public schools?

Would industry move into a state having this law?

Can Arkansas afford to close her public schools?

PAY YOUR 1960 POLL TAX BEFORE OCTOBER 1
TO VOTE AGAINST AMENDMENT #52
IN NOVEMBER, 1960

INDEX

Index

Index